Bioplasticity

Hypnosis: Mind-Body Healing

Joseph Sansone

High Energy Publishing LLC

Fort Myers, Florida

High Energy Publishing,
PO Box 07204, Fort Myers, FL 33919

LCCN: 2014917825

Library of Congress Control Number: 2014917825

High Energy Publishing LLC: Fort Myers Florida

ISBN-978-0-692-31598-9

Bioplasticity is consciousness or the mind's ability to alter or heal the body, including the brain.
Joseph Sansone

Dedication

To Kimberly, with eternal love. May you always be blessed with the Holy Spirit.

Disclaimer

In accordance with the Hippocratic oath, our purpose is first to do no harm. The material presented in this book is not designed to replace or encourage the discontinuance of health care. Always consult with your health-care professional when making decisions regarding your health.

Mind is the Master power that moulds and makes,
And Man is Mind, and evermore he takes
The tool of Thought, and, shaping what he wills,
Brings forth a thousand joys, a thousand ills:—
He thinks in secret, and it comes to pass:
Environment is but his looking-glass.

James Allen

Table of Contents

Acknowledgments

I'd like to acknowledge Dr. Tony De Marco, Dr. John Gatto, Sister Lucille, and the late Dr. John Cardino at the Academy of Professional Hypnosis in New Jersey for their superior instruction in advanced clinical hypnosis back in 1997. When you routinely find yourself at seminars years later saying to yourself, "I know that," it means you had really good instruction. I'd like to express gratitude for the National Guild of Hypnotists and other hypnosis organizations for their tireless efforts to legitimize the profession of hypnotism. I'd also like to thank Tolly Burkan for his instruction in conducting firewalking seminars and, most importantly, sharing his joy of life.

I would be remiss if I did not recognize the countless researchers cited in this book for their pursuit of excellence and furthering of human knowledge. I am certain that many of these researchers faced resistance for even venturing into the study of hypnosis and the other areas cited in this book. Their sense of discovery and curiosity is marvelous.

I am grateful to my family for their support. I'd also like to thank Babu G. for his high-energy friendship. And to Kimberly, whose very presence is an inspiration.

Introduction

The purpose of this book is to be a catalyst to awaken readers to the unlimited potential that rests within them and to gain control over their health—body and mind. It is also written with the express purpose of promoting hypnotherapy or hypnosis as a unique and distinct healing art to the general public.

This is not an easy task, as hypnosis is generally a misunderstood healing art. It is hoped that this book will change that. When speaking to people about hypnosis, I am usually met with one of two responses. Either hypnosis seems interesting, and a person wants to know more, or there is a snicker or a grin and some level of sarcasm. This book is intended for both of these groups. Those with a natural inclination to learn more about hypnosis will do so by reading this book. Those who have a reasonable suspicion will have it allayed after seeing a preponderance of the evidence. The latter group will awkwardly realize how silly it sounds when they say hypnosis isn't real or other such comments.

There are four parts to the following text. Part 1 of the text is an introduction of sorts to the field of hypnotism. In chapter 1, we take a look at hypnosis as a lost healing art. We briefly trace the history of hypnosis from ancient to present times. We also touch on the history of hypnosis relative to the medical and mental health fields.

This leads us to chapter 2 and the topic of the current state of the profession of hypnosis. We examine a couple different views on the profession, ranging from the view that hypnosis is merely a technique to the position that it is a unique healing art. The issue of credibility is also mentioned.

In chapter 3, we approach the difficult topic of defining hypnosis. In doing so, we look at both narrow and broad definitions of hypnosis. We also look at some of the data coming in from state-of-the-art technology.

Part 2 is a review of the evidence that hypnosis is a potent healing modality that can be used to treat a wide variety of issues and to augment current treatments. In this section of the text, we cover mostly published journal articles and a few other credible sources to establish the legitimacy of hypnosis. Essentially, each part of the book is designed to parallel the four parts of a typical hypnosis session. Part 2 of the text is designed to act like an intellectual induction that parallels the hypnotic induction.

In chapter 4, the issue of hypnosis and physical health is tackled. In this chapter we examine a broad range of studies on the efficacy of hypnosis relative to a variety of medical issues. The legitimacy of hypnosis as both a stand-alone and complementary therapy is clearly established in this chapter. In chapter 5, the legitimacy of hypnosis is expanded into the area of pain management. Again studies revealing the efficacy of hypnosis as a stand-alone or adjunct therapy to other treatments are reviewed. Chapter 6 takes a quick look at the mental health and behavioral areas where hypnosis is effective.

The unique hybrid treatment of hypnopuncture is reviewed in chapter 7. This is where acupuncture and hypnosis are combined to enhance the efficacy of acupuncture. The issue of performance enhancement is then examined in chapter 8.

In chapter 9, we have a little fun exploring consciousness with hypnosis. Near-death experiences, psychic phenomenon, and past-life therapy are briefly examined. Mass media hypnosis, nocebos, and placebos are the topic of chapter 10.

Part 3 is an open look at some theories behind why and how hypnosis may work. This is designed to parallel the safe place often created in the session. Chapter 11, titled "Bioplasticity," and chapter 12, titled "Healing Fields," are focused on theories behind mind, body, and spiritual healing. Speculation and conjecture are engaged in as these issues are explored.

Part 4 is a brief look at the practical application of some basic self-hypnosis techniques, which of course is designed to parallel the work or suggestion part of a hypnosis session. In chapter 13, the process of releasing illness and disease is considered, as is the affirmative and imaginative process of healing. In chapter 14, language and affirmations are considered. In chapter 15, a basic self-hypnosis process is described, and in chapter 16, a few final thoughts on healing and spiritual growth are considered.

While hypnosis and hypnotherapy are demonstrated in this book as potent healing therapies for a wide range of issues and effective with an even broader range of people, we are in no way promoting a one-size-fits-all template. Nor are other healing arts and therapies being disparaged. Hypnosis is demonstrated in this book to be an effective stand-alone therapy and an effective adjunct to other therapies. While hypnosis and hypnotherapy are extremely effective with many people, it is evident that some treatments work better for some than others. Like all things in life, it is up to the individual to discover which therapies and treatments work for them and which don't. It is also important to point out here that when hypnosis is mentioned as a stand-alone treatment, that simply means that it can be effective in certain situations on its own and not as an adjunct. These are cases when other treatments are not effective or not desired for some reason. It is not necessarily being advocated that hypnosis be used instead of other treatments.

The following text is supported by approximately two hundred sources. Most of these sources are peer-reviewed journal articles. Other facts cited come from credible sources. Anecdotal stories and testimonials have been kept at a minimum in order to keep the text tight and focused. The factual data that is reviewed in this text demonstrates the potency and legitimacy of hypnosis and mind-body healing. Still, this book is not a journal article. While supported by facts, I do offer opinion here as well.

It is my hope that the reader will come away from this book feeling a greater sense of self-discovery and gain a greater insight into the depth of their mind and spirit. It is also desired that the reader will become more responsible in a guilt-free way about their own health. The intention is that the reader will become more aware of the ideas and concepts they allow into their awareness and begin a process of creating a healthier mind and body in a deliberate fashion. It is also desired that human bioplasticity becomes an idea and concept that promotes further investigation into the nature of consciousness and human potential.

Part 1: An Introduction to Hypnosis

In part 1 of this text, we will briefly examine the ancient roots of hypnosis. In doing so, we find ourselves in ancient Greece and the emergence of Western medicine. Then in chapter 2, we are examining the status of the profession of hypnotism and hypnosis in general in our modern era. In chapter 3, we deal with the conundrum of defining hypnosis and look at the latest state of the art findings on the topic.

Life is hypnosis, just different states of hypnosis.
Joseph Sansone

Chapter 1: The Lost Healing Art

Hypnosis as a healing and therapeutic technique has been employed in virtually every primitive culture since the beginning of human origins. The process of inducing or altering belief systems via trancelike or hypnotic states has routinely been performed across cultures, although the terminology and procedures varied (Schneck, 1954). The process of healing through altering beliefs seemed to universally contain a spiritual or religious element, regardless of locale.

In fact, hypnosis was used throughout the ancient world. Greece, India, Egypt, China, the Americas, and sub-Saharan Africa all used hypnosis. In Greece the cult of Asclepius or Asklipios, who was a poet philosopher, thrived by 500 BC and had a thousand-year history in total. His two sons followed in his footsteps, creating a tradition of Asklipian physician priests. Although a real person, he was later deified as a son of Apollo as the cult grew, spreading to Rome and elsewhere along the Mediterranean, including Carthage and Egypt. Even Socrates belonged to this cult, with his final dying words a tribute to Asclepius (Machovec, 1975).

Hippocrates, the father of modern medicine, was an Asklipian priest physician. He practiced in the Aegean at the temple of Kos. It is from him that we have the Hippocratic oath. He authored eighty-seven works, detailing healing processes and removing it from supernatural causes to more natural causes or etiology. His four personality traits were later adopted by Pavlov. Hippocrates taught his physician priests to use what is now called the scientific method to diagnose and treat illness.

Not as widely known, Asklipiades was another Asklipian priest who placed emphasis on diet, exercise, bathing, and cleanliness and was an early pioneer in the concept of mental health (Machovec, 1979).

Machovec also tells us that the Asklipian cult was in major competition to early Christianity; Asklipian was also depicted as a compassionate and gentle healer. The Greeks believed him the kindest of the gods.

In Greece these cult temples were set outside of the cities in tranquil settings along streams, among the trees, surrounded by nature on elevated ground. This setting was designed to assist the relaxation process necessary for hypnosis. With healing waters and exotic stones from far off places to construct the temples, only those with clean minds or imbued with faith and higher thoughts were instructed to enter the temples. This supportive atmosphere literally set the stage for hypnosis.

Temples had an inner sanctuary for the priests and an outer room for those being healed. The entrance of the temple was decorated with the sleep god subduing a powerful lion with his hypnotic power. Testimonials of cured patients were stationed outside the temple on tablets for all to see.

An inventory of the patients' physical status was taken, and herbs and ointments were used. Patients would undergo a sleep-induced healing process. Healthy diets were often prescribed. Exercise was also prescribed at times. The hypnotic induction process was long because it was actually acted out in ritualistic fashion. Ceremonial bathing and then rhythmic massage led up to the dream healing state after the lights were extinguished. Dressed ceremoniously with a staff in one hand, snake in the other drifted from patient to patient, calming them to sleep if they were awake and providing suggestions to them if they slept, no doubt facilitating the healing process and reported visions of the patients.

Machovec points out that the healing therapy entailed an environmental change, physical cleansing, sacrifice, repetition, investment and faith in the therapy, focused attention, and emotional impact. For more hypnotizable subjects, the effect would be potent. For less hypnotizable subjects, at least a minimal effect would occur. It was a combination of cognitive, affective, behavioral, social, physical, and spiritual therapies.

Machovec also tells us by reporting on the work of other researchers that the Egyptian physician priests used hypnotic techniques in their practice. Combined with drugs and ritualistic prayers and strong sensory stimuli, they drove away evil entities. They were using the multifaceted psychological conditioning to cause a subconscious change in the patient.

He also recounts the Babylonians' astoundingly simple and practical hypnotic approach to healing. They would send their infirm to the marketplace, where they would sit reclined all day. Throughout the day, both friends and strangers would stop by and speak to them about their illness and give advice and suggestions about how they recovered from similar conditions. This repetitive process of healing suggestions would assist recovery.

Ancient Indian yogis have been employing altered states of consciousness since at least 200 AD. Meditation is similar to hypnosis, although they are also distinctly unique states of consciousness. However, there is clearly an overlap between the two. There are countless applications of hypnosis, as there are countless variations of meditation. Many types of meditation are guided and become a similar and often identical process as hypnotic-guided imagery. They do use repetitive chants and incense, chimes, and other sensory stimuli to deepen the meditative state in many, Zen, Tibetan, and Buddhist traditions.

Machovec does also point out the use of drums, chanting, and rhythmic movements common to North American Indian tribes and sub-Saharan African cultures designed to induce altered states of consciousness. Shamanic healing has been going on for thousands of years assisting healing, controlling pain, slowing down blood loss, facilitating childbirth, and addressing mental health issues. It also has strongly embedded hypnotic component (McClenon, 1997).

This hypnotic suggestion may not entail the clearly defined verbal suggestions often used in modern hypnotherapy. Ancient shamanic healing may or may not involve other forces we are not aware of; however, the hypnotic element is often symbolic, striking a subconscious chord. There is also of course an altered state induced by previously mentioned methods.

This pretechnological prehistoric world of magic, faith, wisdom, and superstition can easily be imagined. It must have been an exciting period in certain respects, filled with mystery and discovery around every corner. Out of this primordial organic soup of human understanding emerged all the great disciplines of the modern human intellect. These early spiritual and religious traditions gave birth to science, medicine, philosophy, politics, mathematics, literature, and civilization itself.

These ancient cultures in unrecorded history must have endured the cycles alternating between enlightenment and oppression and upheaval that we see today. They must have experienced ages of growth and prosperity and leaps of knowledge, then only to see their versions of Marxism, fascism, socialism, and other forms of authoritarianism crop up in times of scarcity and weakness, destroying knowledge and prosperity, tipping the scales so far that chaos ensued, fertilizing the ground for a new period of growth and expansion.

This cycle likely repeated itself countless times at various stages of human development in different locations around the globe throughout prehistory. Each time it occurred, with ever increasing stakes, it lost so much that was gained; new directions must have been sought. Sometimes sophisticated cities for the technological age perished in the sands of time; other times cultures collapsed that we might scarcely notice the setback if we knew they existed.

It may have been that somewhere along this journey traversing between tyranny and chaos, that each new form of intellectual discipline was born. With the new discipline breaking away from the old, distancing it from the once high ideas that descended into superstition and oppression, ancient versions of the European Reformation and Counterreformation, bifurcating child from parent at each turn. Emerging schools of thought competing for its understanding of the truth to triumph, finally birthing new disciplines altogether, disjointed from its origins.

It just may be a difficult habit to break. Ideas that reveal a higher level of understanding at one point in time become an ideological chain at a later time preventing another intuitive leap in understanding to express itself. A large part of human history is that of an individual or a group of people leaving another group of people and creating something new.

In the current diversification of intellectual disciplines the collaboration of fields of study has been stifled. Experts are forced into corners, unable to express their creativity across fields of study as they should. Disparate ideologies have emerged in the sciences that are completely untenable. Even what science is has come under debate. Is it an honest and open search for higher truths or a reactionary faith in materialism and a rigid belief in the orthodoxy of its various fields of study?

Through this process of societal and cultural evolution, the intellectual attempts to create an objective reality distinct from its subjective origins have extended beyond its limits. In the efforts to create the illusion of an objective reality, we have discarded our own power, our ability to influence our bodies and our minds. We have retained our faith in the magic potions, but have disregarded the power of our own thoughts and beliefs regarding our physical and mental health.

The idea that thoughts and beliefs were instrumental to healing and physical regeneration was a given to primitive man (Cleland, 1953). To the modern world with its advances in technology, this paradigm of reality has been lost. Science, however, is beginning to reestablish this link. Quantum physicists, cosmologists, and even some biologists are now questioning the material reductionism view of reality (Sheldrake, 2012). Some physicists have even presented a more holographic view of the universe (Bohm, 2008).

There is also a greater emphasis on thoughts and emotions and their accompanying beliefs to have an effect on the material environment. This seems especially true with regard to the human body. The arbitrary distinction between mind and body has once again become gray in some areas of scientific endeavor.

A scientific revolution is currently underway that may not formally be recognized for decades yet to come. Its implication on the world we live in and how we perceive it is still unknown. Until these seeds of intellectual thought sprout, we need demonstrate for the modern thinker empirical evidence that hypnosis is both real and effective. First, let's take a very brief look at some of the names associated with hypnosis in modern times.

Ironically, like its ancient shamanic roots, the modern roots of hypnosis are traced back to physicians. Possibly the most famous hypnotist in the Western world was a German physician named Franz Anton Mesmer. In the seventeen hundreds, Mesmer achieved notoriety for his use of hypnosis techniques for healing purposes. At the time it was called mesmerism. Mesmer was also known to employ theatrics. Rightly or wrongly, Mesmer was discredited by his contemporaries. Since then hypnosis has been under a cloud of suspicion (Spanos, 1982).

It should be noted that Mesmer's healings weren't actually discredited; only his theory of an invisible fluid of some sort was discredited for lack of proof. He believed in what he called animal magnetism, which included a transfer of energy between both animate and inanimate objects. Blockage of this invisible fluid could cause illness. Originally, he actually used magnets, but later he just relied on animal magnetism via mesmeric passes with his hands.

Part of the problem with Mesmer was that his assertions appeared to mix truth with confabulations. This could have been purposely, a product of ego inflation, or simply self-deceit or adhering to false assumptions. Or it could have been a mixture of all of the above. There clearly was a phenomenon of inducing a trance state that did occur. It is also important to remember that at the time the use of bloodletting with leeches was still in practice and that Mesmer's therapy must have seemed completely alien to the practice of medicine of the day.

It might also be worth mentioning that a loosely similar concept of electromagnetism is now cutting edge neuroscience and psychotherapy with transcranial magnetic stimulation (TMS) (Martens, Koehler, & Vijselaar, 2013). Also, Mesmer's concept of a blockage of this invisible fluid called animal magnetism causing illness is similar to the idea of a blockage of the life force, or *chi,* as causing illness in acupuncture. It is possible that he somehow perceived or intuited these acupuncture channels and was able to either manipulate them or get his patients to manipulate them via mesmerism. The evidence in favor of acupuncture meridians will be discussed later. Regardless, we may never know the motives of Mesmer or his thought processes in theorizing about how his approach worked or in how he developed his technique. We do know that his techniques worked to a degree. We also know that his efforts resurrected this ancient healing art.

In 1838 in the United States, Phineas Parkhurst Quimby first became acquainted with mesmerism. Having witnessed a public demonstration, he then began experimenting himself. By 1840 this experimentation increased, and between 1843 and 1847, Quimby began his own public demonstrations. Dr. Quimby was recorded to have healed numerous people with mesmerism. Originally he thought there may have been a transfer of an invisible fluid, as Mesmer claimed. Over time he realized that it was suggestion and the changing of beliefs that was the cause of the healings. Afterward he gradually moved away from mesmerism as a healing approach and instead opted for a completely spiritual approach toward healing (Quimby, 2008).

Dr. Quimby's healings were recorded by many newspapers and verified by physicians and surgeons. There is also a body of evidence of letters written by patients thanking him for their cures. He healed patients dealing with a variety of chronic and incurable illnesses. Many of Quimby's patients were left to let nature run its course by their doctors. Dr. Quimby seems to have had great success treating these patients who were essentially left for dead or a life of extreme limitation. Quimby had a room full of crutches and canes from former patients who were restored to walking.

Unlike Quimby, whose method was noninvasive, James Esdaile was a British surgeon practicing in India at the time who first attempted mesmerism in 1845. Out of desperation to ease a patient's pain during surgery, he used it successfully as analgesia. Amazingly this feat was done based on his readings on the topic; he had never seen it demonstrated.

Esdaile reports that the people in India were very susceptible to mesmerism (Esdaile, 1846). He attributes it to their depressed state of their nervous system as a result of being undernourished and lacking nervous energy. Most likely it was due to their experience with meditation and a greater likelihood to believe in a mental treatment for physical illness. Whereas Western thought attributes positivism or observable reality as the only thing we can know, instead of the external objective reality, Hinduism asserts that the only thing we can truly know is mental experience, and all other assumptions are speculation and conjecture (Scotton, Chinen, & Battista, 1996). Imaginably, this would produce less conscious and unconscious resistance toward healing through mental faculties.

Esdaile thought mesmerism was probably an ancient form of healing that existed since the early origin of man. Esdaile successfully used mesmerism for many types of illness and surgeries, including as an analgesia for many surgeries, including amputations and eye surgeries (Esdaile, 1846). In a time before Pasteur, Esdaile was highly successful at using mesmerism by giving suggestions to avoid infections while operating on patients.

James Braid was a Scottish surgeon that expanded the frontiers of hypnotism also in the mid-1800s. He had experimented with self-hypnosis and showed that hypnosis was a technique in itself and did not depend upon the animal magnetism of the practitioner. His work influenced other physicians of the time. He also was the first to use the word hypnotism. In late 1841

Braid actually investigated a case of mesmerism or animal magnetism, as a skeptical inquirer put it. He discovered aspects of the phenomenon that added a degree of credibility to it. He thought he would be able to write a paper on it in the medical section of the British Association. His hope was to foster an open dialogue and learn from others what their thoughts were on some of the mysterious mechanisms involved, to get the medical community, including himself, to decipher the phenomenon in an unbiased way (Braid, 1843).

Unfortunately, his idea of approaching the topic with fellow professionals in a scientific manner was rebuffed discriminately. However, many members of the association did express interest in the area of investigation. Out of economy he invited all of the members to attend as he read the rejected essay and demonstrated experiments for those who came. After witnessing the event, the chairman of the association affirmed support, and a vote of gratitude was passed for sharing the knowledge.

Braid sought to separate hypnotism from mesmerism or animal magnetism to remove bias for or against the phenomenon. He viewed hypnotism as a simple and quick remedy to alter the body's nervous system, allowing a cure to certain diseases and medical conditions. Quite clearly and responsibly, he thought hypnosis was an additional tool for healing, not a cure all for every ailment or disease. Braid did not know whether hypnosis was solely guided by the imagination or by other means. He did state that no other treatment appeared to control the imagination as hypnosis did, especially with such rapidness to change the bodily condition with a thought or word.

It is quite telling that the initial response prior to his demonstration to the association was disdain. This appears to be a recurrent pattern in the sciences. When strongly held dogmas are challenged by new inquiry, many so called scientists prefer to not look at the evidence.

Understandably, Braid reassured his readers that hypnosis could only be performed with consent; people could not be hypnotized against their will in a clinical setting. Unlike drugs, which could be used to subdue a person, hypnosis didn't work that way. He also advocated that professional only should use hypnosis, for it may not be warrantable in certain cases.

One thing that Braid did was show that a specific induction process, in his case eye fixation, was responsible for the hypnotic phenomenon, not mesmeric passes or a transfer of a magnetic fluid of some sort. His inductions would sometimes take only a few minutes. He was also regularly successful in inducing hypnosis, while those that practiced mesmeric passes were not as often successful.

Eye fixation is still sometimes used today; however, it is often not used and not necessary. A hypnotic induction can begin with the patient or client's eyes open or closed completely. All of Braid's ideas about why and how hypnosis works are not correct. Actually, even today, the mechanisms behind hypnosis are not fully understood. He was a pioneer in the field, and his contribution was to systemize an efficient process of induction and use it effectively in medical cases, especially those that were refractive to other treatments and even in surgery in a day when effective anesthetics were not available.

Braid also showed that the hypnotist did not have some absolute power over the subject. He demonstrated that the patient's free will was necessary to participate in the process. This was a marked difference from the mesmerists who professed the ability to manipulate people by secret passes from a distance. He also categorized many of the physical symptoms that are helpful for the hypnotist to recognize the presence of the hypnotic state on the participant. In essence he brought the field of hypnosis out from the purely mystical into the scientific domain and established a more professional basis for the field of study.

Braid considered the few cases of hypnosis not working by his method to be one of resistance on the part of the participant. He did acknowledge that variety in susceptibleness and the effectiveness of hypnosis among individuals, with some people only being able to reach lighter states of hypnosis and enjoy less effective degree of suggestibility.

With the advent of ether and the birth of chemical anesthesia, the interest in hypnosis waned considerably. Once again this magnificent healing therapy was sidetracked. This strangely potent healing therapy gave way to the age of pharmacology. Unlike the European experience of hypnosis, where it was introduced or reintroduced in the 1700s and 1800s by the medical field, in America, hypnosis was introduced by way of demonstrations and stage hypnotists to the public. "Lay hypnotists" who were either stage hypnotists themselves or taught by stage hypnotists, in turn taught the medical and psychological community the healing art of hypnosis from the 1800s to the mid-1900s. It is difficult to determine how much this fact contributes to the resistance toward the profession of hypnotism in the United States.

William James was born in 1842 and died in 1910. James, whom many consider the father of American psychology, was heavily influenced by the transcendental movement. He was interested in hypnosis, and he did establish the legitimacy of altered states of consciousness and mystical or peak experiences (James, 2009). James also implied a potentially metaphysical subconscious mind that may be a direct connective link with God or spiritual reality.

Sigmund Freud in the late 1800s and early 1900s of course had contributed tremendously to the field of psychology with his psychoanalytic theories, but also to the field of hypnosis with his views on the unconscious mind. He did, however, disregard hypnosis, although he did employ waking suggestions in his sessions. And unlike James's view of the subconscious as a kind of interface with God, Freud's less enlightened view presented it more as a reservoir of sexual desires and impulses than of having any kind of metaphysical quality, although Freud did not totally dismiss mystical experiences, and may in fact of been employing his version of mindfulness with his "evenly suspended attention" during psychoanalysis (Bruce, Allen, & John, 1996). James's view is more closely in line with the typical consulting hypnotist of today, who if not attaching a spiritual or metaphysical significance to the subconscious, will likely view it as unlocked potential at the very least, rather than as something to be restrained.

In the early nineteen hundreds, a pharmacist and psychologist, Emile Coué, pointed out that the imagination will always defeat the will when in competition. He illustrates this point effortlessly with the example of placing a plank of wood on the ground that anyone could walk across. When that plank of wood is placed at a high altitude, the simple task becomes nothing of the sort as the imagination engages in images of falling to death or serious injury. When the plank was on the ground, we imagine we can simply walk across; when it is high in the air, we imagine otherwise (Coué, 1922).

Incredibly, Coué, in his book on self-mastery through auto-suggestion, advocated prenatal care with this device. As we shall see later, he was not far off the mark. His advice for hypnotists was solid; he also particularly advocated that they always act confidently giving suggestions while believing they could help the patient.

Whether suggestions are given in a commanding tone or a more permissive tonality will vary in effectiveness based on personality type. Keep in mind that different techniques will necessarily reflect the age that they are employed in. After all, it is the meaning we attach to words that grants them their power.

Emile Coué was also known to teach self-hypnosis to his patients, thus enhancing the personal empowerment aspect of hypnosis. A famous affirmation he taught was "Every day, in every way, I am getting better and better." He viewed the hypnotist as a friend who guides the patient along the way. Most hypnotherapists today teach their clients self-hypnosis to be used in between sessions and after they have ended their professional relationship as well. He thought that an idea that is focused on will come to fruition if it is possible. His suggestions were always positive and empowering. It was this emphasis on both empowerment and developing suggestions that was a major contribution to the field of hypnosis.

Another well-known hypnotist of the twentieth century worth mentioning, Arthur Ellen, was known in the 1900s for assisting athletes and actors. He helped actors like Tony Curtis remember their lines and Nolan Ryan, the fast-ball pitcher, with pregame jitters. He used a very conversational style of hypnosis (*LA Times*).

Andrew Salter also was a psychologist and was one of the first well-known opponents of psychoanalysis (Salter, 1949). He promoted hypnosis, using Pavlov's techniques of behavioral therapy. He gained early recognition for successfully treating alcoholics.

Milton Erickson was a psychiatrist known for his unconventional treatments. He specialized in medical hypnosis and understood that the unconscious was always listening, even when we aren't aware of it. He would also use permissive rather than authoritarian suggestions in his hypnotic induction and employed confusion techniques as well (Erickson, 1964).

Conclusion

In this chapter we have taken a look at the history of the lost healing art of hypnosis. This was in no way an exhaustive review. Instead, it was a very brief overview of the origins of the hypnosis.

When considering where the healing art of hypnosis sits in the mind-set of the general public as we conclude this chapter, there are a few things to consider. Stage hypnotists, while credited with introducing hypnosis to the public in America, have also encouraged much fear, ignorance, and suspicion toward the field of hypnosis. The suspicion toward hypnosis may continue partly due to the potential threat that hypnosis poses to the traditional healing modality or scientific paradigm that much of the medical and mental health communities operate under. While some may look at hypnosis with intrigue, the questions it raises may cause discomfort for others.

Also, the idea that our thoughts, emotions, and beliefs have the ability to change, or alter, or control our physical well-being places an enormous amount of responsibility on the individual. If the emphasis of individual responsibility for one's health is wrongly applied a great amount of guilt, and self-blame can result. The current material reductionist pharmacology-based model of illness and healing does the opposite, placing the blame for illness and disease on externals. It also gives credit to an external remedy for physical healing. While this removes responsibility, it is also disempowering.

Chapter 2: The Profession of Hypnosis

Hypnotism as a healing art straddles the physical and mental health fields. It is a unique healing art in this way. However, recognition as a legitimate profession has been an uphill battle. Other professions have managed to limit its use or prohibit its use in certain instances unless practitioners also belong to other established healing arts. Still, in the last thirty years or so, great strides have been made to promote hypnotism as a distinct profession, consulting hypnotists, the preferred term by the National Guild of Hypnotists, operate throughout the United States and in over eighty countries.

In many ways the profession of hypnosis is like an automobile that has been stolen and had its parts sold off on the black market. In some states hypnosis is not regulated; in other states it is regulated. Regulations tend to be moderate to very restrictive. In Florida, for instance, therapeutic hypnosis is prohibited for hypnotists unless they belong to another healing art (Law.onecle.com). Practitioners of the various healing arts are allowed to practice hypnosis as long as they stay within the confines of their specific healing art. Of course, where they learned hypnosis is an entirely different issue.

To give an example of the ambiguity, we can look at the state of Florida. Hypnosis is not recognized in Florida as a healing therapeutic art. It is considered more of a technique. The profession of hypnosis has not been lobbied out of existence, but it has been marginalized to a degree in this state. However, the definition of hypnosis is a little vague, and the definition of "therapeutic" is not existent in the law. And Florida law seems to protect hypnosis for nontherapeutic use. As a result, "lay" or consulting hypnotists can operate in Florida although they must exist within this ambiguous framework. They can assist people as consulting hypnotists being very careful of the language they use and steering clear of what would be considered obvious pathologies and therapeutic use. However, much variety of opinion exists on what is considered therapeutic. Consulting hypnotists can engage in therapeutic hypnosis for mental or medical disorders if they receive a referral from the appropriate health-care provider. Similar situations exist in other states; however, the breadth of latitude varies according to nuances in the local law.

Other states have more or less restrictive laws. According to the National Guild of Hypnotists, currently it appears that the following states are unregulated: Alabama, Delaware, Georgia, Indiana, Iowa, Kansas, Kentucky, Louisiana, Maine, Massachusetts, Michigan, Nebraska, North Dakota, Oklahoma, Oregon, Pennsylvania, South Dakota, Vermont, Virginia, and Wisconsin.

The following states have indirect laws that prohibit therapeutic hypnosis unless it falls within the scope of practice for another healing art, but they don't prohibit nontherapeutic hypnosis: Alaska, Arkansas, Arizona, District of Columbia, Hawaii, Maryland, Mississippi, Missouri, Montana, New York, Ohio, South Carolina, Tennessee, Texas, West Virginia, and Wyoming.

And the following states have specific regulations dealing specifically with hypnosis: California, Colorado, Connecticut, Florida, Idaho, Illinois, Minnesota, New Jersey, New Hampshire (regulation voluntary, otherwise guild standard), New Mexico, Nevada (forensic hypnosis only), North Carolina, Rhode Island, Utah, and Washington (NGH.net). The National Guild of Hypnotists was formed in 1951. This nonprofit organization exists to promote the profession of hypnotism as a distinct healing art. It also cooperates with other groups to promote hypnosis in general.

Laws are constantly changing. It is wise that any hypnotist reading the above list of states consult with legal counsel on current laws. We are not giving legal advice here or anywhere else in this book; we are simply attempting to illustrate the current landscape for the profession of hypnosis.

While principally the lack of regulation of hypnosis or any profession is the ideal state of existence from a sophisticated understanding of the First Amendment freedom of association point of view, and also from a sophisticated free-market economics point of view, the reality is that regulation may be necessary to protect hypnotists from overzealous state governments and other professions. Regulation is typically argued to protect the public, but regulation may be required to protect the profession of hypnosis, which would indirectly serve the public. The current regulations have marginalized the profession of hypnosis and have adversely affected the public, because the regulations have assisted the underutilization of hypnotherapy in alleviating mental and physical distress. It may be that this process needs to be reversed.

The underutilization of hypnotherapy by current professional fields does help make the case that hypnosis should be recognized as a unique healing art in the same fashion that chiropractic medicine and acupuncture is. In the case of acupuncture, some states give very little recognition to the healing art, but others give acupuncturists similar standing to medical doctors. Chiropractic medicine has achieved a more stable professional status.

As already stated, the field of Western medicine actually arose out of the ancient Greek practice of hypnosis in the Asklipian cult. And this relationship has gone full circle; it was the medical field that rebirthed hypnosis in its modern Western form a few hundred years ago. Modern psychotherapy could arguably also be a byproduct of the rediscovery of hypnosis.

Hypnosis, as a unique healing art straddling both the mental health field and the medical health field, is a very cost effective and much-needed therapy. Clearly we are not advocating the diagnosis of medical issues by nonmedical doctors or the prescribing of medications. Nor should hypnotists take it upon themselves to discourage other treatments or therapies. However, it is this author's view that a consulting hypnotist should be able to provide medical hypnosis as an adjunct or even a stand-alone therapy for nonacute conditions if that is what a person wants and there is fully informed consent.

Eight states have passed health freedom laws (NationalHealthFreedom.org). California, being the largest state to pass such a law, did so back in 2001. These laws vary, but essentially they allow people to seek alternative and complementary mind-body therapies from unlicensed persons. It appears that the unlicensed person needs to disclose that they are not licensed and can't engage in any kind of invasive treatment. In the eight states that have passed health freedom laws, it appears that hypnotists can in fact use their skill and healing art to assist a person with physical illness.

Health freedom laws are an attempt to restore the basic human right to freedom of association guaranteed in the First Amendment of the US Constitution. Health freedom laws are also an attempt to allow free-market competition to play a role in the health-care market. Unfortunately, there are still forty-two states that have not protected practitioners' rights to offer their alternate or complementary services and the public's right to seek them. Government licensure and interference with the free market and freedom of association looks like it is here to stay for the time being. However, this trend may change as health freedom laws may gain traction over time.

It is not economically feasible for most medical doctors to spend the time with patients using hypnosis for healing purposes. Unfortunately, when they start their practices, they are strapped with exceptionally high student loans and other costs that have severely crippled their flexibility on how they model their business. Even if medical doctors did have the flexibility to spend the amount of time necessary to incorporate hypnosis into their practice, many of them are not open to holistic therapies that challenge the mechanistic view of health. And many who are can't afford to dilute their time in this manner.

It appears in the current centrally controlled climate of government and academic authoritarianism that one possible way to augment the profession of hypnosis to a legitimate status as a unique healing art and stand-alone profession for physical and mental health therapeutic purposes, would require increasing the educational requirements. At the current time most hypnosis programs are certificate programs and at best are approved vocational level schools at the state level by the departments of education. Presumably this would entail grandfathering currently certified hypnotists and coming up with a credentialing organization that would approve university and college programs that would be suitable for state licensure. Apparently, forcing people into debt and allowing a small group of people to cash in on it is the only way to legitimize a profession in America.

The fate of the profession of hypnosis is not clear. At the moment, the odds are not clear that its full recognition as a unique healing art will come to fruition. It may be that recognition as a stand-alone therapy or stand-alone profession for therapeutic purposes may or may not happen. There is a vested financial interest among other professions to prevent competition from a new profession. Unfortunately, this is also aided by a lack of education and understanding of hypnosis among many mental health and medical professionals.

Currently, the American Society of Clinical Hypnosis, a smaller and newer organization than the National Guild of Hypnotists, but also a legitimate organization that promotes hypnotherapy, holds the position that its members must in fact be licensed professionals in the mental health or medical fields and have a master's degree, at a minimum, the exception being student members (asch.net). This position support hypnosis as a technique and is antagonistic toward the profession of hypnotism as a unique healing art or profession. The fact that hypnosis appears to have been introduced in America by public demonstrations and stage hypnotists and taught to the medical and psychological communities by lay hypnotists clouds this position a little.

This is clearly at odds with the National Guild of Hypnotists, which has nearly fifteen thousand members, and its efforts to promote the profession of hypnotism. Even with the muddied water and ambiguity that surrounds the profession of hypnotism, the guild has been successful in legitimizing the profession of hypnosis and consulting hypnotists to a great degree and now even has its own union for hypnotists. Their stated goal is to make going to a consulting hypnotist who helps regular people with everyday problems a regular and normal occurrence, just like going to the dentist or a chiropractor.

As already stated, when it comes to serving the public, the best argument for hypnosis being recognized as a unique healing art is its lack of utilization by other professions. Conversely, regarding the public, the best-case scenario is to increase the use of hypnotherapy within the current healing arts or professions and to establish hypnosis as a unique healing art as well. This author's purpose is to promote hypnosis in the most feasible way possible. It may be that both promoting hypnosis through the current healing arts and simultaneously promoting the profession of hypnosis is the most efficient way to benefit the public until greater recognition of hypnosis as a stand-alone profession is achieved.

The ideal situation would be formal recognition of hypnosis by state licensure agencies as a distinct and unique profession and healing art and the allowance of other professionals trained in hypnosis to incorporate hypnotherapy into their practice. This would benefit the public the most by mainstreaming hypnotism into the health-care community while at the same time not precluding overlapping professions from using hypnosis in their practices. Currently the market for hypnosis is being restricted, since many professionals who are licensed don't offer hypnotherapy as part of their practice. Many who practice hypnosis or want to offer hypnosis services are restricted by the same licensure laws, since the profession is being censored. The allowance of the hypnosis market to grow along with the creation of more competition and alternatives would offer the public the most competent treatment at the highest monetary value possible.

Consumers would have the option of going to their current health-care professionals who practice hypnotherapy if desired. They would also have the choice of going directly to a professional hypnotist if desired. A professional who specializes in hypnosis may provide an attractive alternative or complementary treatment to those being rendered by other professionals. When we get to defining what hypnosis is, it will also become apparent that restricting the use of hypnosis in the current various professions is just as egregious as restricting the profession of hypnotism. This is because while hypnosis is, in fact, a unique state of consciousness, it should also be viewed on a continuum. Either way, our purpose is to promote this lost healing art. It is to dispel many misconceptions about it. It is also to educate on its broad range of applicability.

Hypnosis as a therapy does fall within the scope of practice of psychologists and mental health counselors in most if not all states. Right now there is mostly a unidirectional relationship between the medical and mental health fields. Medical doctors can readily treat mental illness and prescribe medications or other therapies. This, of course, makes perfect sense, since the body does affect the mind.

However, it is not quite as established that those in the mental health field can treat physical illnesses as an adjunct for the specific purpose of healing the illness. There needs to be wider acceptance of the bidirectionality between the mental health and the medical fields. If the illness is determined to be psychosomatic, then it is considered all right to treat the mind to alleviate the symptoms. However, it is not quite as often asserted that treating the mind and the restructuring of beliefs and mental processes is a natural treatment for medical conditions. Of course, the passage of the health freedom laws mentioned above would easily resolve this.

The evidence presented in this book supports the notion that the distinction between mind and body is not so clear. It also is supportive that the mind, at a minimum, wields an influence equal on the body as the body wields upon the mind. It therefore must fall within the scope of practice of the mental health fields to treat nonacute medical conditions from a psychological or mental health paradigm.

Arguably, it already does fall within the scope of practice for mental health professionals to treat the mind in order to assist physical healing; however, this scope of practice is not often asserted. The evidence presented here will, I hope, assist those in the mental health field to assert the efficacy of treating the mind to treat the body. This is being advanced not in the spirit of competition with the medical field, but in the spirit of cooperation. An integrative approach toward well-being is the best.

Conclusion

The profession of hypnotism has come a long way thanks to the efforts of the National Guild of Hypnotists and many affiliated and unaffiliated statewide hypnosis organizations. As can be seen, there is still ambiguity toward the profession of hypnosis and its status among the licensed professions and the various state laws that limit its use.

It is hoped that the evidence presented in this book will act as a catalyst to some degree toward the continued mainstreaming of the professional field of hypnotism, and mainstreaming hypnotherapy as a commonly used treatment among psychologists, mental health counselors, and physicians, for mental health and medical health issues. As will be demonstrated, hypnotherapy is a cost-effective adaptive treatment for a wide range of illnesses and conditions.

Chapter 3: Defining Hypnosis

So then, what is hypnosis?

Practically speaking, it can be described as a deep state of relaxation where the mind more readily accepts both conscious and unconscious suggestions. The key ingredients to a successful hypnosis session, besides a competent hypnotist, of course, are the three ingredients of belief, expectation, and motivation on behalf of the client or patient seeking help.

The typical hypnotic session consists of an initial interview and consultation, followed by an induction. The induction usually employs progressive relaxation. This is a process of gradually facilitating the relaxation of the client's body parts via verbal suggestions and visualizations. The clients actively assist the process, since they are normally motivated and seeking help for a mental or even physical issue of some sort.

While a client is in a hypnotic state, hypnosis can be effectively used for a wide variety of issues ranging from motivation, to personal growth, improving sports performance, sales skills, public speaking, enhancing creativity, changing unwanted habits, and treating a variety of mental and medical disorders. It can also be used as an adjunct therapy for a host of medical disorders. These are just a few of the applications for hypnosis in a clinical setting.

Many suggestions given during hypnosis are a form of posthypnotic suggestion—that is, a suggestion designed to have an effect after the hypnosis session has ended. Some posthypnotic suggestions induce conscious amnesia and use the subconscious mind to act on the suggestion. This technique often is accompanied by a trigger or activation signal. Emotional anchors can also be employed. While all clinical hypnosis generally seeks to restructure conscience and unconscious beliefs, an amnesia-induced posthypnotic suggestion relies solely on the subconscious belief being restructured. The idea behind it is that by inducing amnesia, conscious resistance to the suggestion is eliminated, creating a more potent suggestion.

Guided imagery and visualizations are also an effective method used during hypnosis. Actually, many stand-alone therapies can be employed during hypnosis. The net result can often yield a quicker and more efficient outcome for both the therapist or counselor and the client.

Contrary to popular belief, if a client is in a sufficiently deep hypnotic state, they can be an active participant in the session. Meaning, rather than simply sit passively with their eyes closed, they can open their eyes, walk, and talk, as well as write or engage in other activities. It completely depends on the situation, client, and what is being treated as to whether a passive or active hypnosis session is best.

This leads us to some of the controversy surrounding the definition of hypnosis. For instance, is someone acting on a posthypnotic suggestion still in a hypnotic state? Guided imagery is often used as a stand-alone treatment. Clearly it is a technique often used in hypnosis, but does the process of guided imagery itself fall into the category of hypnosis if there is no formal induction that uses the word hypnosis? Often it is called guided meditation, which leads to another issue of the overlap between hypnosis, meditation, and affirmative prayer.

Simply put, just by not using the word hypnosis, it doesn't mean it *isn't* hypnosis. Counselors and therapists or other coaches or teachers often don't use the term hypnosis. Sometimes this is done to avoid legal issues, which *I have no problem with.* And unless the practitioner uses the word hypnosis or employs a very structured posthypnotic suggestion with a trigger of some sort—as I have mentioned in this chapter—it is likely a good loophole.

Other times the word hypnosis is not used to avoid the potential negative associations connected with misconceptions about hypnosis. People not educated about hypnosis have many irrational fears that need to be addressed. They probably have fewer fears regarding guided imagery, guided visualizations, or guided meditation, even though they are all the same thing. The same is also true about self-directed imagery, visualizations, or meditation.

Still, for our purposes, we will consider these all forms of hypnosis and self-hypnosis. If you are sitting in a relaxed state for twenty or thirty minutes, imagining and visualizing an outcome, that is hypnosis or self-hypnosis, whether you call it hypnosis or not. There is, however, research that indicated that using the label hypnosis does in fact make the suggestions more effective (Schoenberger, Kirsch, Gearan, Montgomery, & Pastyrnak, 1998). This is a very logical finding, as many with great misconceptions about hypnosis have them because they have witnessed stage hypnotists demonstrate the power of hypnosis. As a result, the irrational fear is that they can be controlled, yet at the same time when properly it directed assists the belief structures and expectations about the success of a hypnotic intervention of some kind.

It is often said that all hypnosis is self-hypnosis; the hypnotist just facilitates the process. This is because while the competence and skills of the hypnotists are very important, ultimately the power resides in the client's mind, as there is no inherent power in the hypnotist. The hypnotist creates the structural framework to direct or misdirect the mind toward the desired goals of the client. Ultimately, the hypnotist is a guide.

The most rigid materialists argue that there is no such thing as a hypnotic state. They say the whole phenomenon is simply the power of suggestion acting on a willing participant. Many take this stance based on a dogmatic faith in materialism and a rejection of all that may imply that there may be a nonphysical aspect to reality. They take the position that the mind itself doesn't actually exist. There is simply a brain with electrical and chemical impulses and reactions. Their stance is that if it isn't material, it isn't real. Taken to the extreme, the behaviorist point of view is that we don't even have free will and, in fact, only respond to environmental influences. That is the mind-set that is guiding this position to a great degree.

As we journey into our discovery of the lost healing art, let us examine whether there is any real physical evidence that hypnosis is in fact a unique condition of the mind. To do so, we will rely on hard science. We will look into some new research on the topic using magnetic resonance imaging (MRI).

Research at Stanford University School of Medicine has revealed some exciting evidence using functional magnetic resonance imaging (fMRI), bringing them very close to an actual brain signature by showing that areas of the brain associated with executive control and attention have less activity in people who can't be hypnotized compared to people than can be hypnotized (Hoeft, et al., 2012). Their results stated specifically:

> High compared with low hypnotizable individuals had greater functional connectivity between the left dorsolateral prefrontal cortex, an executive-control region of the brain, and the salience network composed of the dorsal anterior cingulate cortex, anterior insula, amygdala, and ventral striatum, involved in detecting, integrating, and filtering relevant somatic, autonomic, and emotional information using independent component analysis. Seed-based analysis confirmed

> elevated functional coupling between the dorsal anterior cingulate cortex and the dorsolateral prefrontal cortex in high compared with low hypnotizable individuals. These functional differences were not due to any variation in brain structure in these regions, including regional gray and white matter volumes and white matter microstructure.

And their conclusion read:

> Our results provide novel evidence that altered functional connectivity in the dorsolateral prefrontal cortex and dorsal anterior cingulate cortex may underlie hypnotizability. Future studies focusing on how these functional networks change and interact during hypnosis are warranted.

Since the research showed that cognitive style was indicated as the common thread rather than personality, it would seem that for the time being, we have to conclude that something physiological does occur during hypnosis, thereby making it a unique state of mind. The researchers said that their experience has led them to estimate that up to a quarter of patients cannot be hypnotized. This is a much higher number than many consulting hypnotists believe true, normally asserting that 3–5 percent can't be hypnotized. However, this may be simply an indication of different ideas about what being hypnotized means. For example, those people only being capable of a light state of hypnosis may be considered hypnotized by some therapists and counselors and not by others. Trust is also a big factor, as is motivation in the ability to be hypnotized. My view is that basically everybody can be hypnotized to some degree unless there is a communication barrier caused by severe autism or Down syndrome or something along those lines. Or simply that the client has a trust issue and refuses to let go, which could potentially have been a confounding variable in the study above.

Others investigators have looked into the time distortion and hallucinations associated with Parkinson's disease and schizophrenia. Both of these diseases have a physiological basis and are considered in an altered state of consciousness while having hallucinations. They suggest that the directed or self-directed hallucinations during hypnosis would therefore also be an altered state of consciousness (Naish, 2006).

Other researchers also conducted a study showing that subjects with high hypnotic susceptibility showed higher theta activity in their anterior temporal lobe groups with lower hypnotic susceptibility (Elahi, Boostani, & Motie Nasrabadi, 2012). Still other research suggests that theta wave activity is associated with relaxation and alpha waves are associated with susceptibility to suggestion (Williams & Gruzelier, 2001).

It is generally thought that hypnosis induces an altered state of consciousness ranging between the alpha and theta states of brain wave activity. Beta is the wave pattern for the waking state, alpha is a relaxed state, theta is a deeply relaxed state and delta is associated with a sleeping state. The cycles are as follows:

Beta (13–40 cycles per second) waking activity
Alpha (8–13 cycles per second) relaxed, light meditation, daydreaming
Theta (4–7 cycles per second) deep states of hypnosis
Delta (0.5–4 cycles per second)

Studies on neuroplasticity (how the brain changes and adapts) have supported this with an EEG that hypnosis exists at the alpha and theta brain wave frequencies (Halsband, Mueller, Hinterberger, & Strickner, 2009). Further studies at MIT may also support the state theory of hypnosis (Rainville, Hofbauer, Bushnell, Duncan, & Price, 2002):

> Regression analyses between regional cerebral blood flow (rCBF) and self-ratings confirm the hypothesized involvement of the anterior cingulate cortex (ACC), the thalamus, and the pontomesencephalic brainstem in the production of hypnotic states. Hypnotic relaxation further involved an increase in occipital rCBF that is consistent with our previous interpretation that hypnotic states are characterized by a decrease in cortical arousal and a reduction in cross-modality suppression (disinhibition). In contrast, increases in mental absorption during hypnosis were associated with rCBF increases in a distributed network of cortical and subcortical structures previously described as the brain's attentional system. These findings are discussed in support of a state theory of hypnosis in which the basic changes in phenomenal experience produced by hypnotic induction reflect, at least in part, the modulation of activity within brain areas critically involved in the regulation of consciousness.

Other researchers' findings showed that highly hypnotizable people demonstrated decreased brain activity in the anterior region of the default mode network. The implication is that hypnotic induction creates a distinctive and unique pattern of brain activity (McGeown, Mazzoni, Venneri, & Kirsch, 2009). While that on its own doesn't prove that it is an alternate state, the evidence from these studies is pointing in that direction. Although these researchers, unlike the previous MIT researchers, state that it doesn't necessarily support or disprove the state theory of hypnosis, I think it is tilting the scale in that direction.

Using sound stimulus tested the fluctuation analysis of EEG's between waking and hypnotic states. The fluctuation analysis revealed a marked difference from hypnosis and the waking state. This too is supportive of the state theory of hypnosis (Lee & Koo, 2012).

A cold pressor pain test is done by submerging the hand in ice water. It is actually a cardiovascular test, as heart rate and blood pressure are measured after placing the hand in the ice water. It is also done to measure pain. Participants let the researcher know when they feel pain, and when it becomes intolerable. The idea is to get a pain threshold and a level of pain tolerance.

Using this test and a test to measure distraction versus hypnosis and waking relaxation, those who were highly hypnotizable had more significant pain relief with hypnosis than with distraction or relaxation. They also had greater pain relief than the less susceptible group. The EEG revealed that the more suggestible participants compared to less suggestible participants had a significant increase in theta wave activity in the parietal and occipital parts of the brain. This is more evidence rejecting the sociocognitive theory.

Quantitative electroencephalographic (EEG) findings showed significantly greater high theta (5.5–7.5 Hz) activity for highs as compared to lows at parietal (P3) and occipital (01) sites during both hypnosis and waking relaxation conditions. The findings fail to support the sociocognitive conceptualization of hypnotic behavior while providing additional evidence supporting the neodissociation theory. This theory proposes a dissociation of control and an altered state of consciousness. It also does not support the sociocognitive theory that claims that hypnosis is not an altered state of consciousness and is simply the acting out of expected suggestions within a certain context (Freeman, Barabasz, Barabasz, & Warner, 2000).

While no scientific theory or hypothesis can ever truly be proved, it either gains support with new evidence that emerges, or it loses support with new evidence that emerges, and the theory or hypothesis either gets amended or discarded. The evidence from several scientific studies presented in this chapter while not proving it, is supportive that hypnosis is a unique state of consciousness. Discarding this evidence may be indicative of cognitive dissonance, which is a social psychology theory that people, often when presented with evidence that challenges their strongly held beliefs, simply may deny the evidence and cling to their beliefs more rigidly (Festinger, 1962).

Research done at Cornell University using fMRI showed that posthypnotic suggestion reduced activity in the anterior cingulate cortex and in areas of the brain associated with visual activity (Raz, Fan, & Posner, 2005). In this instance, a posthypnotic suggestion was given to counteract the Stroop effect by suggesting that all words would appear in gray scale. The Stroop effect is a delayed reaction time in naming colors that appear in words stating a different color. For instance, if the word red was written in yellow ink, people are more likely to have a delayed reaction time stating the color and are more prone to errors.

This study is intriguing because it not only showed decreased activity in the anterior cingulate cortex and areas associated in visual activity, coinciding with the suggestion altering perception of the color of the words, but it also occurred during the posthypnotic suggestion.

This leads back to the question: What is hypnosis? There was an alteration in brain activity that occurred both during hypnosis and while the posthypnotic suggestion was active while reducing the Stroop effect! Instead of adversely affecting the argument that hypnosis is a unique state, this aids the position that hypnosis is multidimensional and is supportive of my quote earlier stating that *life is hypnosis, just different states of hypnosis*.

We will touch on this concept further along in our journey into the lost healing art, but for now, consider that hypnosis has many dimensions and is not always structured. Hypnotists often use the term "waking hypnosis" to describe the process of interviewing a client and setting the stage for the hypnotic suggestions by initiating the proper suggestions prior to a formal induction. In a normal waking state we are all affected by the power of suggestion, in both verbal and visual forms. Keep in mind that people do enter semihypnotic states while watching television, listening to music, driving a car, and a host of other activities.

It may be that people who are not good subjects for hypnosis were actually more susceptible to the power of suggestion while in the waking state. There is no evidence to support that. It would require a whole new set of experiments to justify that statement, and it is beyond the scope of this book.

Last, I would be remiss if I didn't include the American Psychological Association (APA) definition of hypnosis as follows (APA.org):

> According to the American Psychological Association's Division of Psychological Hypnosis, hypnosis is a procedure during , a health professional or researcher suggests while treating someone that he or she experience changes in sensations, perceptions, thoughts, or behavior. Although some hypnosis is used to make people more alert, most hypnosis includes suggestions for relaxation, calmness, and well-being. Instructions to imagine or think about pleasant experiences are also commonly included during hypnosis. People respond to hypnosis in different ways. Some describe hypnosis as a

> state of focused attention, in which they feel very calm and relaxed. Most people describe the experience as pleasant.

For now, we can define structured hypnosis as an altered state of consciousness where the mind is more susceptible to the power of both verbal and visual suggestions, and the altering and restructuring of unconscious beliefs is more easily accomplished, as is the altering of perception, both during and after the hypnosis session. This enhanced power of suggestion has an impact on both mental and physical symptoms.

In this part of the book we have taken a look at hypnosis as a lost healing art by very briefly examining the history of hypnosis dating back to the Asklipian cult in ancient Greece, and with it the birth of modern Western medicine. We've touched on the modern and distinct profession of hypnotism and where hypnosis stands today. And we've just seen that credible research exists that is supportive of the stated theory of hypnosis, further legitimizing hypnosis as real.

Still, what about its efficacy? Does hypnosis actually work? To answer that question we must continue on our journey in part two of this book and examine in more detail some of the studies that demonstrate that hypnosis does work. To do so, let's take a look at the research involving cancer and the immune system in the next section of this book.

Part 2: The Evidence for Hypnosis

In part two of this book, we are presenting the evidence that hypnosis is, in fact, a real and potent healing modality. We will be highlighting medical or physical issues that have been successfully treated with hypnosis. This includes pain as well as mental health issues. The information provided here is based mostly on peer-reviewed scientific journal articles and a few other very credible sources. Performance enhancement, exploring consciousness, and other areas are also presented.

We won't bother addressing readers with unreasonable doubts. There just simply isn't much that can be done in such cases. The purpose of this section of the book is to lend credibility to any reasonable doubts that a reader may have regarding hypnosis. This is why we have focused so intently on peer-reviewed journal articles. However, it is worth pointing out more than once that most hypnotists don't do research, and most researchers don't do hypnosis. As a result, in many areas the efficacy of hypnosis in this section of the book may be understated.

The scientific method requires that all the evidence be looked at; however, for the reasons just stated, many cases never get reported or make their way into journal articles. Also, many cases of what is often called spontaneous healing never get reported either. These often entail a mind-body or spiritual component whether actual structured hypnosis is involved or not. It is the view of this author that although this section of the book should be an eye-opener for the average reader who is not very familiar with hypnosis, the efficacy and the scope of hypnosis, although deliberately done so, is probably being understated here.

Physician, heal yourself.
Luke 4:23

Chapter 4: Hypnosis and Physical Healing

In this chapter we will look at a host of physical issues where hypnosis has been used successfully across a wide variety of physical infirmities. Most of the information regarding hypnosis in this chapter comes from published articles in scientific journals. The exceptions are from highly credible sources.

The intent is not to present hypnosis as a panacea or the next magic pill. It is simply to enlighten the reader to the incredible range of use and adaptability of hypnosis. Arguably, there is no other treatment that has such a broad scope and applicability with no known side effects.

Hypnosis, Cancer, and the Immune System

The immune system, as we know, is the body's defense system against diseases and foreign invaders. Scientists continue to learn more about the human immune system every day, but there is still much that we don't know. The official definition according to (NAID) the National Institute of Allergies and Infectious Diseases (NIH.gov):

> The immune system is a network of cells, tissues, and organs that work together to defend the body against attacks by "foreign" invaders. These are primarily microbes—tiny organisms such as bacteria, parasites, and fungi that can cause infections. Viruses also cause infections, but are too primitive to be classified as living organisms. The human body provides an ideal environment for many microbes. It is the immune

> system's job to keep them out or, failing that, to seek out and destroy them.

In the case of cancer, cells divide, grow uncontrolled, form tumors, and spread to other body parts. Or through the lymphatic system or bloodstream the uncontrolled cell division can spread throughout the body. The official definition at the National Cancer Institute (Cancer.gov):

> Cancer is a term used for diseases in which abnormal cells divide without control and are able to invade other tissues. Cancer cells can spread to other parts of the body through the blood and lymph systems.
>
> Cancer is not just one disease but many diseases. There are more than one hundred different types of cancer. Most cancers are named for the organ or type of cell in which they start—for example, cancer that begins in the colon is called colon cancer; cancer that begins in melanocytes of the skin is called melanoma.

They go on to describe the main types of cancer as

1. carcinoma—cancer that begins in the skin or in tissues that line or cover internal organs; there are a number of subtypes of carcinoma, including adenocarcinoma, basal cell carcinoma, squamous cell carcinoma, and transitional cell carcinoma;
2. sarcoma—cancer that begins in bone, cartilage, fat, muscle, blood vessels, or other connective or supportive tissue;
3. leukemia—cancer that starts in blood-forming tissue such as the bone marrow and causes large numbers of abnormal blood cells to be produced and enter the blood;

4. lymphoma and myeloma—cancers that begin in the cells of the immune system;
5. central nervous system cancers—cancers that begin in the tissues of the brain and spinal cord.

There is an overlap between the blood cancers and the immune system, and the immune system is intricately entwined with cancer resistance, which is why we are looking at both issues together.

When case studies exist outside of main scientific precepts, they are often labeled anecdotal evidence rather than called case studies, which is what they are. There are many instances of people who benefited from self-induced healing. There are also cases of people who were given up for dead by their doctors and likely used a form of hypnosis, guided imagery, and prayer and recovered to complete health.

These cases should not be ignored and require further investigation. We might actually argue that these cases, rather than being ignored, are the ones that should be studied the most. Instead, they are set aside as we scratch our heads. They are so baffling that they aren't considered healed or cured, only in remission.

Our focus is not on these types of cases. This is partly because the self-induced healing or remission cases don't usually end up in scientific papers. It is also because we want to build a more systematic case for hypnosis as a most effective healing art.

We are looking at more structured scientific studies. There are positive and negative aspects of this approach. It limits what can be observed. It would be clearly unethical to not provide traditional treatments for cancer and use only hypnosis to one control group and utilize another control group with patients only using traditional treatments. On the other hand, the results we will look at are quantifiable, even if they are not always isolated.

Before we examine controlled studies there are a few case studies worth mentioning because they were reported by Bernie S. Siegel, MD, a well-respected reliable source who won't be doubted, in his book, *Love, Medicine, and Miracles*.

In one instance a patient was hypnotized and while in hypnosis was guided to imagine valves that controlled blood flow. The patient was then directed to cut off the blood supply by switching off the blood supply to the cancerous tumor. The pain went away, and the tumor was reduced to one-fourth its previous size. The patient was released. Unfortunately he did die of complications during a later surgery, but it was discovered that his metastatic cancer had vanished, and the grapefruit-size tumor was now the size of a golf ball.

He reports another case of a patient with advanced throat cancer who was receiving radiation treatment. He imagined his treatments and improving his white blood cells positively, and incredibly, he did not experience bad side effects, and the cancer vanished. This patient later managed to use the same approach to rid himself of chronic arthritis that had afflicted him for twenty years.

Siegel reports on another extraordinary case of a child with an inoperable brain tumor who was sent home after radiation did not rid him of the tumor. Here the child was guided to imagine rocket ships flying around in his head, shooting at the tumor. The tumor vanished entirely (Siegel, 1998).

Siegel tells us that it is important that individuals pick visualizations that works for them. If they are not comfortable with the imagery, the effect may be limited or even negative.

The imagery of shooting cells or other conflict type imagery may work for some, but may be counterproductive than others.

The Rev. C. Scot Giles, D.Min., started the first hospital-based medically approved program for the treatment of cancer in 1991 (Giles, 2003). This long term hypnosis cancer program is based on the work of Bernie Siegel. The three basic concepts are to explore a person's explanatory style, their inner dialogue, and their conflicts. The second concept is of unconscious awareness, allowing expression and insight to come forth. And the third basis is using illness as a metaphor, learning, and growing through the illness.

Hypnosis is prominently featured in this ICAN program, and sessions are conducted weekly with tapes to take home for reinforcement if desired. Giles reports 57.9 percent surviving at the thirteen-year point. These are extremely impressive numbers considering that most patients were at progressed stages and not early stages of cancer when they joined the program. Giles points out that the success rate is distributed across the program's timeline, and the surviving patients are not mainly newly admitted patients into the program. The long-term success rate is steady over time.

Research on breast cancer survivors showed that hypnotic induced guided imagery had a positive effect on psychological well-being and immune system function (Bakke, Purtzer, & Newton, 2002). Natural killer cells (NK cells) were measured before and after an eight-week training program using hypnosis-induced guided imagery. NK cells function in the innate immune system as T-cells function in the adaptive immune system. They respond to cells infected with viruses and attack tumor formation.

The absolute number of NK cells did increase after the hypnosis-induced guided imagery. When the treatment stopped the effect wore off. Researchers concluded that there is a place for hypnosis-induced guided imagery as an adjuvant therapy.

Another study on breast cancer patients consisted of two groups. Both groups of patients underwent chemotherapy, surgery, radiotherapy, hormone therapy, but one group was taught relaxation and guided imagery. The group that was taught the self-hypnosis technique of guided imagery had more activated T cells and LAK cell subsets. Mature T-cells were significantly higher in the group that used guided imagery. Those that rated their guided imagery experience highly had elevated NK cell activity after chemotherapy and follow up as well as LAK cell activity. The frequency of the relaxation was also correlated to the number of T-cell helper cells (Eremin, et al., 2009).

This is astounding, though, in that it shows that hypnosis, and for that matter, the mind itself, can enhance the immune system function—in this particular case, the immune system's cancer fighting ability. This has broad implications about individuals' roles in their own healing process and in both the preventative and maintenance aspects of maintaining good health. It also shows that the distinction between the mind and body is not concrete. It is interactive. As the body can affect the mind, so too can the mind affect the body.

Another case study reported by Steven Gurgevich, PhD, was of a woman who lived in Arizona. She was an RN and being familiar with the side effect, she had decided that she didn't want to get chemo for her breast cancer. She had noticed that the dry riverbeds where she lived turned into powerful flowing rivers when on rare occasions it did rain. In hypnosis the imagery of a powerful river washing away the cancer cells was used successfully to rid the woman of her cancer. Gurgevich also reports a case of a woman who did receive chemotherapy for her cancer. She did not want to lose her hair from the treatment and sought him out. Fortunately he was successful in treating her with hypnosis, and she did not lose her hair from the chemotherapy (Weil & Gurgevich, 2005).

Further evidence of the positive effect of visualization on the immune system showed that white blood cell count (WBC) increased significantly with patients diagnosed with cancer, AIDS, viral infections, and other medical conditions associated with depressed WBC count (Donaldson, 2000). The patients did not receive any other treatment during this study that should have altered their WBC.

Patients in this study were trained in a thirty-minute audiotaped program inducing general relaxation suggestions and specific suggestions and imagery. They then listened to the thirty-minute tape once a day. The group that consisted of ten females and ten males of varying ages all showed positive results. Initially as predicted all the subjects showed a decrease in WBC thirty minutes after the first session and five days after the first session. However, they all showed increases in WBC in thirty days. After sixty days WBC increased more, and after ninety days there was a very significant increase in WBC.

The researchers postulated that the initial drop in WBC as they predicted may have been due to a process called marginalization where they initially migrated to the areas of greatest need. This in itself is quite fascinating, because it would mean that as early as thirty minutes after the first taped hypnosis session the guided imagery had an effect.

Once again, the researchers didn't use the word "hypnosis," but the tape had suggestions for relaxation and for visualizations, and patients were either sitting or lying down with their spines strait. As mentioned in the first chapter, guided imagery is a form of hypnosis, so as a reminder we will treat them the same moving forward. The same applies for the previous study.

It is also intriguing that people of different ages with different diseases all showed significant increases in WBC over the ninety days, though some patients were included in the study who stated that they did not believe that the guided imagery would have a positive impact on WBC given their current state of health. It is possible that their response to the survey before the study exhibited a conscious belief that conflicted with their unconscious beliefs. It could be that the beliefs started changing during the first hypnosis-guided imagery session. Or it is possible that the visualizations can have an impact disconnected from the beliefs of the person doing the visualizing. This seems less likely.

As can be imagined after what you just read, a study of perfectly healthy participants, it was shown that just three sessions, which included posthypnotic suggestions, hypnosis showed an altered T-cell response (Wood, et al., 2003). During hypnosis, suggestions for optimally balancing the immune system were given. Posthypnotic suggestions were given for reducing stress and for continuing an optimally balanced immune and neuroendocrine system.

A meta-analysis of several controlled studies has supported hypnosis as a significant approach toward reducing chemotherapy-induced nausea and vomiting (Richardson, et al., 2007). Among terminally ill cancer patients, hypnosis also produced better quality of life, less depression, and lower anxiety compared to patients that received standard care (Liossi & White, 2001). Hypnosis-guided imagery prior to surgery for patients getting neck and head operations reduced blood loss, hospitalization after surgery, and complications from surgery (Rapkin, Straubing, & Holroyd, 1991).

Another controlled study using cognitive behavioral therapy combined with hypnosis showed that hypnosis was effective at reducing fatigue in patients undergoing radiotherapy for breast cancer. At the end of radiotherapy, during the four-week follow-up, and after six months, the hypnosis group had decreased fatigue. Researchers concluded hypnosis and cognitive behavioral therapy was effective, had no side effects, and continued to have a positive effect long after the treatment ended (Montgomery, et al., 2014).

Inflammatory Bowel Disease and Irritable Bowel Syndrome

Inflammatory bowel disease (IBD) is considered an autoimmune disease. The body's immune system in this case attacks elements of the digestive system. The two main types of IBD are Crohn's disease and ulcerative colitis. The main difference between the two is that ulcerative colitis attacks the colon. Ulcerative colitis is restricted to the colon and rectum and to the lining of the gut, whereas Crohn's disease is not so limited and can present itself in any part of the gastrointestinal tract. As imagined by the name, IBD can cause ulcers, abdominal pain, anemia, vomiting, bleeding, cramps, and bloating. It is a difficult disease to diagnose because it has a great variety on how it presents itself.

Gut-focused hypnotherapy has had positive effects on IBD. Hypnosis has shown to have a dramatic increase in quality of life with 79 percent describing quality of life as good or excellent. Hypnotherapy has shown to bring about complete remission in as many as 26 percent of patients suffering from the disease. As an adjunct therapy it may be very effective and can spare the need for taking steroids. Nearly 60 percent of patients stop taking corticosteroids (Miller & Whorwell, 2008).

To be able to have patients reduce or even stop using steroids or other drugs, is in itself a remarkable and positive outcome. Many of these drugs are quite frankly, experimental. The long term effects of using them and the potential contraindications and negative interactions with other drugs are hard to calculate.

Another related—though less severe condition—that hypnosis has had a positive effect on is irritable bowel syndrome (IBS). IBS doesn't cause the inflammation that IBD does; the digestive system isn't working as it should and has many similar symptoms. Gas, bloating, pain, diarrhea, and constipation are all associated with IBS. It is considered a functional disorder and is still difficult to pin down because of the idiosyncratic ways its symptoms show up. Mounting evidence clearly supports that hypnosis is an efficacious treatment for IBS. The positive effects appear to be long lasting and medication is decreased over the long term. The mechanism of how hypnotherapy works is still elusive, however (Gonsalkorale & Whorwell, 2005).

Functional dyspepsia is a chronic indigestion that impacts up to 15 percent of the population by some estimates. Hypnotherapy has also been shown to be very effective in as a long-term treatment for functional dyspepsia. A controlled study involving 126 patients were placed in three random groups. Hypnotherapy, other support therapy and a placebo, and a dedication group over a sixteen-week study. Hypnotherapy significantly outscored the other two groups for short term treatment, with that significance increasing with long term treatment. Amazingly, 90 percent of the medical group, and 82 percent of the support group continued medication during follow up; none of the hypnotherapy group participants did (Calvert, Houghton, Cooper, Morris, & Whorwell, 2002).

Pregnancy and Childbirth

In vitro fertilization is a process where a sperm fertilizes an egg in a laboratory. It is a procedure used to aid in pregnancy for couples dealing with infertility issues. An embryo transfer is a step during in vitro fertilization when the embryo is transplanted into the uterus.

Hypnosis during embryo transfer has demonstrated a 76 percent increase in pregnancy ratios compared to a control group during in vitro fertilization (Levitas, et al., 2006). Suggesting that hypnosis during embryo transfer may significantly improve the in vitro fertilization embryo transfer cycle outcome in with both increased implantation and clinical pregnancy rates. Relaxing the uterus during the embryo transfer likely reduced embryo displacement. Patients also had a more favorable outcome toward the procedure.

Further research involving hypnosis and embryo transfers suggests it is as effective as diazepam in terms of pregnancy ratio and relaxation, noticeably with fewer side effects (Catoire, et al., 2013).

Hypnosis in childbirth itself has also been effective. Compared to control groups in which 53 percent used epidurals while 36 percent of women taught self-hypnosis in preparation for child birth. The women taught self-hypnosis also required less augmentation (Cyna, Andrew, & McAuliffe, 2006).

Generally, in childbirth, self-hypnosis is taught to women leading up to delivery. Its purpose is twofold: to reduce anxiety and stress, and to reduce pain and discomfort during birth. Often a technique called glove anesthesia or analgesia is used. This is when the patient is taught a specific procedure to anesthetize the hand mentally and then learn to transfer the loss of sensation to other parts of the body by placing their hand on the body part. A trigger can then be learned to induce it when desired. It is an interactive process between the hypnotherapist and the client that requires practice. Posthypnotic suggestions are often used too in hypnosis sessions prior to childbirth.

Having a hypnotist present facilitating the hypnosis session during the childbirth, as it is done during embryo transfer, is not typically done. That being said, it is sometimes done. It is also apparently effective on patients with no prior practice being hypnotized. Patients individually hypnotized during active labor who weren't hypnotized prior to going into labor, required only a twenty-minute induction, and the total time added to the delivery by the hypnotic procedure was forty five minutes. Compared to the control group, hypnotized patients required less medication and experienced less pain (Rock, Shipley, & Campbell, 1969).

It is safe to imagine the efficacy of hypnosis would be increased dramatically if patients worked with a hypnotist prior to childbirth training them in self-hypnosis and rehearsing the interaction between hypnotist, patient, and medical staff during delivery. Triggers could be reinforced by the hypnotherapist while practicing over a few weeks prior to birth and employed during the actual procedure, as could guided imagery prior and during the delivery process.

According to the Centers for Disease Control and Prevention (CDC), one in nine babies in the United States, almost half a million, are born preterm. Approximately 35 percent of infant deaths are preterm-related deaths (CDC.gov). That is the highest single cause in the United States. Preterm births are also the leading cause of neurological conditions for newborn babies and they are at risk of being born with many other birth defects. The CDC estimates the health-care cost is $26 billion a year.

When labor occurs before thirty-seven weeks of pregnancy it is considered preterm. Any woman can have a preterm baby, but there are certain risk factors that may increase the chance of it happening. If a woman is carrying multiples, has had a preterm baby before, or is having issues with her uterus or cervix, she is at increased risk for a preterm baby. Drinking, drugs, smoking, working late hours, and standing too long at work or elsewhere could be contributing factors, as could late or no prenatal care. Also, medical conditions such as sexually transmitted infections, diabetes, high blood pressure, being underweight, and a list of other potential causes pose a higher risk of a preterm baby.

Hypnosis is not only effective at increasing enjoyment of labor and reducing stress and pain, both meta-analysis and controlled trials indicate that hypnosis is effective at prolonging pregnancy and treating preterm labor. Hypnosis has been shown a number of times to stop preterm labor (Corey Brown & Corydon Hammond, 2007).

If preventing preterm births was the only avenue where hypnosis was regularly used, it could potentially have a tremendous economic impact, and it could save the lives of many newborn babies and possibly prevent the pain and anguish that accompanies children born with birth defects through the course of their lives and the trauma their families endure.

Hypnosis in childbirth also resulted in shorter stage-one labors and higher Apgar scores (Harmon, Hynan, & Tyre, 1990). An Apgar score is a test done a few minutes after birth to assess the health of the newborn baby. There are five criteria that are rated each from zero to two, totaling ten for all five criteria. Seven or above is considered a healthy score. Complexion, pulse rate, reflex, respiratory rate, and activity are all rated. Other research, involving 520 participants in first or second trimester, compared a control group that received attention to a hypnosis group that was given prenatal hypnotherapy. The hypnosis group had better outcomes and fewer complications (Mehl-Madrona, 2004).

Hypnosis and Visual Improvement

We have already learned that hypnosis can alter visual perception, as it did by reducing the Stroop effect. Hypnosis may also have a positive effect on eyesight. In 1967 an accidental discovery involved a hypnotic participant of an experiment not having to do with improving vision or the giving of suggestions for visual improvement of any kind. This participant reported the next day that he was struck by the clarity of the objects he observed during the hypnosis session the day before. Normally he wore his glasses, but the day before, when he was being hypnotized, he was not wearing his glasses.

Two weeks later the participant underwent an ophthalmological exam during hypnosis. It showed that the participant did indeed show significant improvement in vision during the hypnosis session compared to his normal waking state. Again, no suggestions for visual improvement were given (Davison & Singleton, 1967).

This is actually a good example of the fact that hypnosis, even more than other therapies or treatments, can have varying results with different people. The mechanisms underlying hypnosis are not yet understood and neither are the unconscious beliefs of participants. It is likely that both may never be understood. These unseen variables add a certain level of uncertainty but can be reduced during the prehypnosis interview, although that usually deals with a participant's negative misconceptions. The unseen variables also at times reveal the unconscious misconceptions of researchers as well, as the potential for hypnosis affecting vision probably didn't occur to the researcher.

In this scenario the participant's vision could have improved simply because the relaxation of the hypnotic state reduced eye strain, which could account for the significant improvement of his vision during hypnosis. Or the participant could have had subconscious or unconscious beliefs about the hypnosis experience that even he was unaware of that may have accounted for the visual improvement.

There has been research not involving structured hypnosis that supports the notion that belief can alter vision. This research showed that priming participants with the mind-set that pilots have good vision, and then testing participants while in a realistic flight simulator, showed an improvement in vision compared to the control group (Langer, Djikic, Pirson, Madenci, & Donohue, 2010). When participants adopted the role of pilots, their vision improved, compared to those who did not adopt the role of pilots. Another group that was primed with the mind-set that athletes have better vision than nonathletes tested better for vision while doing jumping jacks, as opposed to a group that was skipping, which was thought to be a nonathletic activity.

A final group was tested with the priming inherent in an eye chart. The mind-set is that the farther down the chart, the harder it is to read the letters because they get progressively smaller with each line. The letters were reversed on the test with each line. They were tested with eye charts with smaller letters appearing in the top lines. Participants were able to read some of the smaller letters with the reversed chart that they normally could not read.

This may be as much an example of the power of suggestion as it is the power of priming, as they are somewhat related. Priming may be more of an indirect suggestion. It is a suggestion that is often implied and more contextually based. The implication is that altering beliefs may in fact alter physiological restraints on vision. Many psychologists use the term priming, but a hypnotist may simply call it waking hypnosis.

It should also be noted that the mind's ability to affect optical changes has been demonstrated in cases of people afflicted with (DID) dissociative identity disorder (Miller S. D., 1989). In these cases individuals demonstrated significant changes in optical ability dependent on which alter ego was being tested. The implication again can be drawn that unconscious beliefs can manifest physical changes in the body.

This proposition should not seem like too much of a surprise at this point in our journey. With the exception of a couple studies mentioned, where the simple relaxation of the hypnotic state may have been a factor, it should be apparent that altering beliefs via suggestion is the common thread. The method of suggestion and imagery may change, but changing the underlying belief is the key.

Hypnosis has been demonstrated to have a positive outcome on nearsightedness. Hypnotic suggestion and posthypnotic suggestion both improved vision by reducing nearsightedness. Those with the poorest vision had the greatest improvement with hypnotic suggestion. The visual improvement did transfer out of the laboratory-induced hypnosis and was exhibited in a normal waking state. Another group of highly suggestible participants was not hypnotized but was given similar suggestions and had an equally positive visual improvement in the laboratory. The visual improvement in this group, however, did not carry forward to the nonexperimental setting, as the other group receiving the posthypnotic suggestions experienced (Graham & Leibowitz, 1972).

The simple power of suggestion—or what hypnotists sometimes call waking hypnosis—was effective at improving vision among a highly susceptible group. Still, the effect was lost after they left the experimental situation. This illustrates the power of posthypnotic suggestions and further establishes that there is something unique about the hypnotic state that renders the suggestions more effective. In this study it was shown with the posthypnotic suggestion.

Steven Gurgevich, PhD, tells us about a unique situation involving a patient referred to him by Andrew Weil, MD. In this unique case the individual had burned off his cornea in an accident. There had been four attempts at transplanting a new cornea, and each time the man's body rejected it. Further attempts at transplantation were postponed while being treated with hypnotherapy. While hypnotized over several sessions Gurgevich used an ideometer finger response with the man to determine when his subconscious mind was ready to accept the transplant. Once the response was positive, a new transplant was scheduled, and it was a success (Weil & Gurgevich, 2005).

This case has broad implications regarding hypnosis and organ transplants. It may be that hypnosis could be regularly incorporated into the transplantation protocol when appropriate to eliminate or lessen organ transplant rejections. In some cases drugs may not be needed, or at least lessening the dosage and the side effects.

And finally, regarding hypnosis and vision, physician James Braid did document several cases of patients who saw improved vision after being treated with hypnosis (Braid, 1843). It is likely that hypnosis can be effective to assist many people with impaired vision to varying degrees.

Hypnosis and Tinnitus

Tinnitus is a disorder that causes a ringing or noise in the ears or head. It can be caused by many issues, including neurological ones. The exact physiological cause is still undetermined. The possible culprits range from cardiovascular disease to wax buildup in the ears. The leading cause of tinnitus is noise. Construction workers operating machinery and fire fighters, for instance, are at a higher risk to get the disorder.

Tinnitus may be concomitant with congenital hearing loss or accompanied by noise-induced hearing loss. It is a symptom and not a disease. It is not the cause of hearing loss. The disorder can be intermittent or constant, which can cause much greater distress. It can also be mild to very severe.

In the United States, fifty million people have tinnitus, with sixteen million at a level of severity that prompts them to seek medical attention. Of these, approximately two million have tinnitus to the point where functionality on a day-to-day basis is impaired (ATA.org).

There is no cure for tinnitus. Hypnosis has been effective at treating debilitating tinnitus (Gajan, et al., 2011). Participants recorded beneficial results immediately after hypnosis and long afterward. The efficacy of self-hypnosis was compared to masking and attentiveness to the patients' complaints. Self-hypnosis significantly reduced tinnitus severity compared to the masking and attentiveness group (Attias, et al., 1993). The other treatments had little to no impact.

In a twenty-eight-day inpatient treatment model for treating tinnitus, hypnosis was used successfully. The severity of tinnitus was assessed at admission, discharge and three and six months after discharge. After discharge 90.5 percent of those with subacute tinnitus and 88.3 percent of those with chronic tinnitus had a decrease in severity. The follow-up exams showed stability in the effect of the treatment (Ross, Lange, Unterrainer, & Laszig, 2007).

This may baffle some that a difficult-to-treat disorder like tinnitus can be alleviated with hypnotherapy. It makes total sense logically. Hypnosis is quite effective, as we already know, at altering perceptions.

Skin Diseases

In 1952 a paper was published in the *British Medical Journal* that caused a bit of an international sensation. An adolescent boy who was born with a rare, incurable skin disorder called ichthyosis was treated with success by hypnosis (Mason, 1952). Ichthyosis is a scaling of the skin. The hard dry patches often resemble fish scales.

In the case of this sixteen-year-old boy, it was severe enough that the family turned to hypnosis, after all other remedies, including surgery, were exhausted, with no success. The boys hands were covered with thick, horny casing that were chronically infected due to constant fissuring. The hands, feet, thighs, and calves were the most severe, but the black horny layer covered his whole body except his face, neck, and chest.

While hypnotized the boy was told that his arm would clear. The improvement started in five days, and by the tenth day, the arm from shoulder to wrist was clear. Next the right arm was treated and then days later also cleared; the thick layer came off, and the boy's underlying skin was revealed. Then other parts of the body were treated, and the process of clearing away the casing continued.

There was no relapse, and the boy was able to lead a normal life. Naturally his emotional and social life improved dramatically. Sentenced to a solitary existence before, he now had more normal social interaction and employment.

The hypnotist in this incident was soon inundated with people seeking him out as a last resort to many untreatable illnesses. To the disappointment of many, the same type of results were not achieved. He later said that this rattled him, and he had lost his confidence, which may have affected his results.

This illustrates the unrealistic expectations often sought for in hypnosis. As with any treatment, its results will vary. It is not unusual for people to expect one session to solve their issue. This can happen, but repetition is an important component to successful treatment as is flexibility on the part of the hypnotist and patient.

More common skin afflictions can also be treated with hypnosis. Hypnosis is effective at treating psoriasis. An autoimmune disease, psoriasis affects the skin. The immune system sends out false signals that speed up the growth of skin cells. Up to 7.5 million people are afflicted with it (Psoriasis.org). Usually it shows up as thick red skin with white patches. In a controlled study, chronic, plaque-type psoriasis was treated with significant improvement for highly susceptible participants using hypnosis (Tausk & Whitmore, 1999).

Hypnotherapy also may help treat eczema. Eczema is a type of skin condition similar to psoriasis, although it appears on parts of the body not typical for psoriasis. When compared with biofeedback, hypnosis showed a significant reduction in the severity of surface damage in eczema, although surface area of the skin condition was not reduced (Sokel, Christie, Kent, & Lansdown, 1993).

In children and adolescents with warts hypnosis has been revealed to be very effective. All participants in this study had social problems resulting from their warts. Within three months of therapy, 86 percent were completely cured of their warts (Noll, 1994).

Dr. Gurgevich tells us of an interesting case with a young girl. She unfortunately was having recurring warts on her vocal chords, which, as can be imagined, was quite a health hazard. After several surgeries, each time removing the warts, they had repeatedly retuned. While hypnotized, the girl was instructed to visualize miniaturizing herself and going into her throat to paint or spray the warts with something that she knew would make them disappear forever. When she went in for her next scheduled surgery, they anesthetized her, only to find that the warts had indeed disappeared (Weil & Gurgevich, 2005).

Wound Healing

Hypnosis has been shown to enhance the anatomical and functional healing process of fractures. In this study conducted at Massachusetts General Hospital, both radiographic data and orthopedic assessment demonstrated accelerated healing among participants who received hypnotic interventions. Although a small sample size was used, the results appeared to be conclusive.

Otherwise healthy participants were taken from the emergency department and placed in either a control or treatment group. To test whether hypnosis can accelerate anatomical bone healing, participants were chosen for a site-specific test of bone fracture healing. Participants received regular orthopedic treatment with the treatment group getting hypnotherapy in the form of individual sessions and audiotapes for the purpose of promoting fracture healing.

By six weeks the objective radiographic data showed a noticeable difference in fracture edge healing between the groups, with the hypnosis group outperforming the control group. Orthopedic assessment also showed hypnosis participants had increased ankle mobility and ability to descend stairs by week nine, less pain-killer use when assessed in weeks one, three, and nine, and self-reports reported less pain by week six. Hypnosis appears to assist anatomical and functional fracture healing (Ginandes & Rosenthal, 1999).

There is other evidence of the ability for hypnosis to make anatomical changes in the body. There was a clinical pilot study that looked at rapid hypnotic induction by finger elongation.

The study had sixteen volunteers and five phases that were designed to record both relative and absolute changes to finger length at the conclusion of each phase. There was in fact a significant elongation of the finger, which indicated that the metacarpus, the cartilage between the joints, expanded (Eitner S. W., 2006).

The efficacy of hypnosis as an adjunct therapy for surgical wound healing was further tested among eighteen women undergoing reduction mammaplasty. Among the three groups, postoperatively, one received hypnosis, one supportive care, and another the usual care. The hypnosis group outperformed the other two groups, using an objective medical assessment of the medical incision healing at one and seven weeks by medical staff blind to the group. Clinical exams and scored digital photographs demonstrated a significantly higher healing rate at both one and seven weeks for the hypnosis group (Ginandes, Brooks, Sando, Jones, & Aker, 2003).

Other research indicates hypnosis is effective at assisting burn wound healing (Moore & Kaplan, 1983). Patients selected with symmetrical burns on each side of their body underwent hypnosis directed at assisting healing on only one side of their body, thus leaving the other side of their body as the control. The evaluating medical staff and surgeon were unaware of the hypnosis.

Four out of five patients demonstrated accelerated healing on the one side while the fifth participant demonstrated rapid healing to both sides of the body. I can only guess this participant's subconscious mind cared more about healing than about the study being conducted. In either case, hypnosis was demonstrated to shown as a dramatic facilitator of burn wound healing in this study.

A meta-analysis reviewed hypnosis with surgical patients. The results strongly supported the use of hypnosis. It indicated that hypnosis recipients undergoing a wide variety of surgeries had more positive outcomes than 89 percent of control patients (Montgomery, David, Winkel, Silverstein, & Bovbjerg, 2002).

Stroke Victims

A stroke is often called a brain attack because an artery or blood vessel gets blocked and blood flow ceases to the brain. Brain cells die as the blood flow gets interrupted. The longer the interruption the more brain damage occurs. This is called an ischemic stroke and make up 87 percent of all strokes. Movement, speech, and memory can all be affected by a stroke. The area of the brain where the brain cells die, affect the abilities associated with activity in that part of the brain.

Hemorrhagic stroke is the opposite. Vessels in the brain leak and increase blood flow into the brain. Only 13 percent of strokes fall into this category but they account for 305 deaths. Strokes are the fourth leading cause of death in the United States and there are over seven million stroke survivors. Of the 795,000 strokes that will occur, 133,000 victims will die. And this year fifty-five thousand more women will get strokes, and African Americans have twice the risk for a first-time stroke than whites (Stroke.org).

Warning: after having read the above two paragraphs, take a moment now to reject the information and affirm that it doesn't apply to you. As you must know by now, your mind not only has a say in healing, but in promoting wealth and well-being. Do not adopt the subconscious belief that this applies to you.

A hypnosis study conducted with six chronic stroke participants dealing with learned nonuse of the paretic upper limb resulted in an increased range of motion and grip strength, less spasticity, a more positive outlook and motivation among the participants; there was also more awareness and less effort involved in performing motor tasks (Diamond, Davis, Schaechter, & Howe, 2006). While hypnotized participants used various guided imagery approaches, they alternated between imagining doing the movement prior to the stroke and in the present; they alternated between doing the movement in the present and while actively alert; and they alternated between imagining doing the movement while actively alert and doing the actual movement. Another case study of a stroke victim indicated that after five weeks of treatment with hypnosis, the participant regained full movement of his leg and arm, and improved muscle control in the face (Manganiello, 1986).

A randomized pilot study of stroke victims used two groups. One group with occupational therapy, compared to a group using guided imagery and occupational therapy. All thirteen participants had motor difficulties in the upper limbs and had their stroke between four weeks and a year prior to the study.

Both groups received an hour of occupational therapy at an outpatient clinic three times a week. The group that received guided imagery did so for ten minutes after the occupational therapy on each day and practiced twice a week at home. The group that received both the occupational therapy and guided imagery improved over the six-week trial, while the group that received only the occupational therapy failed to improve (Page, Levine, Sisto, & Johnston, 2001).

We have learned that our brains are plastic. Neuroplasticity is the term given to the brain's ability to restructure itself—even into old age—by changing our thoughts and actions (Doidge, 2007). By exercising the mind and movements of the body, the brain can restructure itself even in people with disabilities and disabling medical conditions resulting from a stroke. This is why physical therapy works with stroke victims.

It is also why hypnosis works. Of course a stroke patient will need to have a certain level of functional ability to allow them to be hypnotized, but through hypnosis they can restructure their mind and regain lost abilities. Like building physical muscles, building mental muscles requires motivation, effort, and repetition. Visualizing something and actually seeing it use similar parts of the brain (Ganis, Thompson, & Kosslyn, 2004). Likewise, mental imagery has a similar blood flow in the brain and autonomic response as doing the physical activity (Decety, 1996).

Hypnosis has been shown to effectively improve motor skills and rehabilitate brain-damaged patients. This rehabilitation is done through motor imagery while hypnotized, and it works even if the patient has impaired or lost the ability to imagine movements. FMRI data supports the efficacy of hypnosis's ability to enhance motor imagery (Müller, Bacht, Schramm, & Seitz, 2012).

So by physically retraining their bodies during physical therapy, stroke patients can restructure their brains and improve motor abilities. And by using hypnosis-guided imagery, they can restructure their brain and regain lost motor skills. This is why imagining the activity and actually practicing the activity can have such a positive impact.

Allergies and Asthma

About 20 percent of Americans are affected by allergies to varying degrees. People can be allergic to anything from pollen, to mold, to foods, just to name a few. Allergies are an abnormal immune response. Symptoms are as varied. They can range from sneezing to hives and rashes (WebMD.com).

Hypnosis is also effective at treating allergies. Participants were taught self-hypnosis and questioned two months later. The result was that 76 percent reported improvement, and of those who used medication 76 percent reported a reduction in their use of medication. Practice was correlated to their improvement (Madrid, Rostel, Pennington, & Murphy, 1995). Hypnosis has also been experimentally shown to be effective at reducing the symptoms of skin allergies (Fry, Mason, & Pearson, 1964).

A controlled experiment using highly susceptible hypnotic subjects was conducted with a histamine skin prick test. Participants responding to hypnotic suggestion had reduced reactions. They also were able to reduce the reaction in one arm and increase it in the other. The objectiveness of this experiment does support hypnosis as effective in influencing allergic reactions (Zachariae, Bjerring, & Arendt -Nielsen, 1989).

A chronic disease that narrows and inflames air passageways, asthma symptoms are often worse at night and in the morning. Coughing, wheezing, restricted breathing, and tightness of the chest are common symptoms. About twenty-five million Americans of all ages have the disease commonly beginning in childhood. Approximately seven million children have it (NIH.gov).

A two-group study was designed to test the effectiveness in treating asthma symptoms. One group was treated with hypnosis, and another with an antispasmodic. Hypnosis was demonstrated as a superior treatment. Hypnosis reduced wheezing and the use of medications. Mild cases did best, as did participants able to achieve deeper states of hypnosis and those who could practice self-hypnosis daily (Maher-Loughnan, Macdonald, Mason, & Fry, 1962).

Hypnosis can reduce the symptoms of bronchial asthma in children between six and seventeen years old. Measuring pulmonary function before, after, and at twice at later dates revealed an improvement of symptoms. The overall average improvement for the group was 50 percent (Aronoff, Aronoff, & Peck, 1975).

Another group study indicates that participants able to achieve deep states of hypnosis and those who are younger have better responses to hypnotherapy. If the asthma has a psychological connection hypnosis may also be more potent. Feelings of well-being are not connected with how severe the symptoms are or how deep the participant was hypnotized, or age (Collison, 1975).

There is support that hypnosis applied in conjunction with self-hypnosis has better results. This study also suggests that hypnotherapy be done prior to steroid use. Asthmatics relying on steroids have poorer results with hypnotherapy (Maher-Loughnan G. P., 1970).

Other findings suggest hypnotic improvement for asthma symptoms that are enhanced by exercise. After running on a treadmill pulmonary functions were measured. The hypnosis group fared better than the control group (Ben-Zvi, Spohn, Young, & Kattan, 1982).

There is a study relative to allergic reactions that clearly illustrates the power of hypnotic suggestion. This involved hypnotic anesthesia. A participant failed to report an allergic reaction that caused one cheek to swell up after receiving a Novocaine injection. A few weeks later when a psychologist was inducing hypnotic anesthesia, a severe reaction causing one cheek to swell occurred after the suggestion was given to achieve numbness similar to Novocain. The psychologist was able to remedy the situation by giving a counter suggestion of a simulated injection as had been done when the original allergic reaction occurred to the real Novocaine injection (Guttman & Ball, 2013).

There are also instances of hypnosis preventing the allergic skin reaction from poison ivy (Barber, 1978).

Angioplasty

Plaque buildup in your arteries is called atherosclerosis. Although the plaque buildup can accumulate in any artery, when it does so in coronary arteries it is called coronary heart disease. Angina or chest pain is caused by the plaque buildup when it narrows blood flow to the heart. If the plaque clots and blocks the artery, it will cause a heart attack.

A procedure to increase blood flow to the heart is called an angioplasty. A thin tube (catheter) is snaked through the blood vessel. Once at the area with the accumulated plaque buildup, the balloon at the tip of the tube is inflated, pressing the plaque against the blood vessel wall, restoring the flow of blood through the artery (NIH.gov).

In a two-group controlled study with sixteen patients in each group, hypnosis reduced pain during surgery. While 13 percent of the hypnosis group required additional narcotics, 44 percent of the control group required additional narcotics during the procedure. The patients who received hypnosis, in contrast to the control group, saw a 25 percent increase in the time the balloon was able to be inflated during the procedure. The hypnosis group also had significantly higher norepinephrine levels (Weinstein & Au, 1991).

Blood Pressure

Hypertension (high blood pressure) is a medical condition where the pressure of the blood flowing through the arteries is too high as it presses against the walls of the artery. It may eventually lead to heart disease.

Your blood pressure is a measurement of how much blood pumped by your heart along with the resistance to that blood flow in the arteries. Many people have high blood pressure for years without knowing it. If it is not controlled, it increases your risk of heart attack and stroke.

Hypertension was the subject of another study that involved hypnosis. A group that used muscle relaxation reduced hypertension. The hypnosis group saw a total elimination of hypertension during hypnosis. Participants were then instructed in self-hypnosis to continue their progress at home (Deabler, Fidel, Dillenkoffer, & Elder, 1973).

Multiple Sclerosis

Multiple Sclerosis (MS) is an immune system disease, a chronic disease, in which the immune system attacks the central nervous system including the spinal chord, optic nerves, and brain. You can experience mild symptoms like numbness in your limbs or more serious symptoms like loss of vision and paralysis. MS is a very unpredictable disease (NationalMSSociety.org).

An interesting case study of a MS patient involving hypnotherapy had promising results. This patient first received psychotherapy because they had very serious denial. Afterward, hypnotherapy was applied. After two weeks, their double vision disappeared, they experienced less pain, and they regained the ability to walk. Hypnotic imagery and posthypnotic suggestions were used. No pharmaceuticals were used (Dane, 1996). A larger study does show that training patients in self-hypnosis is an effective pain management strategy for people with MS (Jensen, et al., 2009).

Parkinson's Disease

Parkinson's disease is of the nervous system and progressive in nature. Tremors, stiffness, and slowing down of movements are the main symptoms. It can often start gradually and be unnoticeable at first. Slurring speech and a flat affect can often be early signs, as can a slight tremor in one hand.

There is no cure, but there are medicines that can alleviate symptoms. Sometimes brain surgery is done to help relieve symptoms. It is considered a genetically based disease, but there may also be environmental triggers (MayoClinic.com).

A case study of a fifty-one-year-old male patient afflicted with Parkinson's disease showed a positive result with hypnotherapy as a treatment for associated symptoms. After receiving hypnosis once a week for three weeks and being instructed in self-hypnosis, sensors revealed a 94 percent reduction in the severity of resting tremors. A subjective patient report indicated improvements in pain, sleep, depression, anxiety, libido, and quality of life (Elkins, Sliwinski, Bowers, & Encarnacion, 2013). A prior case study also supported hypnotherapy with self-hypnosis as an adjunct treatment that reduced tremors associated with Parkinson's disease (Wain, Amen, & Jabbari, 1990).

In a more controlled study of twenty Parkinson's disease patients, relaxation along with guided imagery showed improvement in the tremors as well. The patients all had either moderate or severe tremors. Tremors decreased dramatically in all of the participants (Schlesinger, Benyakov, Erikh, Suraiya, & Schiller, 2009).

Hemophilia

Hemophilia is a disease of the blood. The blood doesn't clot normally, causing prolonged bleeding. The bleeding can be external, as when caused by a cut, or it can also be internal, which can damage organs and tissues in the body; it can even cause death if bad enough. It is normally genetic in nature. It mostly affects men, with approximately one in five thousand having the disease (NIH.gov).

A group of thirty severe hemophiliacs were placed in either a control group or a group taught self-hypnosis. The self-hypnosis was taught over a six-week program and was comprehensive in nature. The group practicing self-hypnosis did significantly reduce the amount of clotting factor concentrate used compared to the control group (Swirsky-Sacchetti & Margolis, 1986).

There was also a case of a very severe twenty-one-year-old hemophiliac who required a tooth extraction, but he was resistant to medications. He did receive anesthesia, and the medication and hypnosis were used also to reduce pain and stop bleeding. The patient who normally required transfusions for the procedure did not bleed anytime. The limited amount of oozing stopped on the fourth day after the procedure (Dubin & Shapiro, 1974).

A larger study also supported that hypnosis was effective in dentistry with hemophiliacs. These patients all received less than the normal replacement therapy. Out of the nineteen patients four required none (Steinberg, Levin, & Bell, 1984).

Raynaud's Disease

A painful disease that affects the blood vessels, Raynaud's disease is rare and most often occurs in the extremities like the fingers and toes. Stress or the cold causes the blood vessels to narrow. The skin turns white or blue from loss of blood flow, and when the blood flow returns, the skin throbs and turns red. In the more severe cases the loss of blood flow can cause tissue death. It is more common for woman and people in colder climates (NIH.gov).

There was a case of a highly hypnotizable participant who saw blood supply increase four times via hypnosis (Conn & Mott Jr, 1984). In a larger study involving thirty-eight participants between the ages of sixteen and seventy-two skin temperature increased during hypnosis spontaneously 1.4 degree Celsius. The skin temperature rose to 2.7 degrees Celsius after the hypnotic suggestions were given. Capillary blood flow increased by 63 percent. Hypnosis and self-hypnosis may be a viable adjunct therapy to diseases requiring increased circulation (Grabowska, 1971). Three of the participants had improvement with Raynaud's disease and twenty-three with diabetes with complications involving blood vessels and circulation.

Diabetes

Diabetes is considered an autoimmune disease. In type 1 diabetes some of the T-cells in the pancreas go rogue and attack the beta cells that produce insulin. This requires those with type 1 diabetes to inject insulin several times a day to reduce blood sugar levels. It is a chronic and expensive disease that causes many complications and reduces lifespan. Although researchers are conducting human clinical trials on what may effectively be a cure (Faustmanlab.org). Type 2 diabetes is equally insidious, though it is less severe. Type 2 diabetes may or may not require insulin or medication and often can be managed by diet and exercise.

The studies above with Raynaud's disease do leave the door open for future research involving diabetes and some of the complications associated with circulation, including neuropathy and retinopathy. Neuropathy can cause pain in the hands and feet and restless leg syndrome among those with diabetes due to poor circulation as a complication of the disease. Retinopathy is the leading cause of blindness among adults. It is the result of poor circulation as a complication of diabetes that causes the vessels in the retina to leak, resulting in loss of detail in the vision.

It is well known that diabetes is affected by diet, exercise, and the amount of insulin taken. The management of this balancing act is also known to be affected by stress. As can be imagined, the multiple variables involved along with their impact is at times difficult to decipher.

Participants with diabetes were hypnotized to reexperience the worst memory of their lives. Their blood sugar was checked every half hour and matched against a control period. Surprisingly, there were significant drops in blood sugar levels as a result of the hypnotically reenacted stress period (Vandenbergh, Sussman, & Titus, 1966). We say surprisingly because stress, which is often associated with poor sugar control for people with diabetes, is also often associated with high levels of sugar in the blood.

Healthy individuals tested after imaginary hypnotic food ingestion had increased insulin in their blood, although there was no change in their blood sugar. For some participants this occurred after hunger suggestions. In others, insulin in the blood increased after eating the hypnotically induced imaginary meal (Goldfine, Abraira, Gruenewald, & Goldstein, 1970).

Once again these two studies support the notion that thoughts, beliefs, and hypnotic suggestion produce physiological changes in the body. However, I think there are further implications specific to the cause of diabetes. Admittedly, this is pure speculation on my part, and I am not a medical doctor.

Type 1 diabetes, as already mentioned, is considered an autoimmune disease. The cause is unknown. And quite frankly it may have multiple causes. Some people think it is caused by vaccines in some way or other external triggers that set off the immune response. This is logical, since as mentioned already, the immune system is attacking another part of the body, creating diabetes. Others think it is more of a genetic propensity or the result of exposure to a virus that causes the autoimmune response. This too is possible.

There may be another potential cause that can operate separately or in conjunction with these other potential causes. The participants with diabetes in the first study above—who reenacted the most negative and stressful period of their lives—saw blood sugar levels fall. This drop in blood sugar levels may have occurred through some kind of muscle memory of the original event or by morphic resonance. As the mind reenacted the stressful period, the body, for lack of a better word, was tricked into reenacting its physiological response that occurred during the initial stress period.

Assuming this stress happened over a long period of time or repeatedly, especially at a young age, it may have caused a prolonged period of lowered sugar levels. If it did, then the immune system may have seen the overproduction of insulin as a threat to the health of the body. The rogue T-cells then attacked the beta cells that produce insulin.

Similarly, in the second study with healthy people just mentioned above, there may be an explanation for type 2 diabetes. There may also be an explanation for the dramatic increase in type 2 diabetes. These healthy people saw an increase in insulin in their blood after either receiving the hypnotic hunger suggestion or eating the imaginary hypnotic meal. If there is a repeated increase in insulin in the blood over a prolonged period, it may cause a similar, though less severe, autoimmune response that impairs insulin production if the immune system perceives the increased insulin as a threat.

There is a connection between heavy television viewing and type 2 diabetes (Grøntved & Hu, 2011). Without discounting the bad eating habits or sedentary lifestyle that may also be associated with increased television viewing, there may be another explanation. When people watch television they are in a semihypnotic state (don't argue with this if you have ever bought something advertised on TV that you didn't need), and they get bombarded with constant food advertisements that induce hunger and simulate eating to spur people to imagine eating food. These television ads may, in fact, create a small increase of insulin in the blood of healthy people that over time could create low sugar levels invoking an immune response to kill off insulin-producing beta cells. This less severe response results in type 2 diabetes.

One approach toward treating diabetes with hypnosis-guided imagery and verbal suggestions would be to attempt to emulate the treatment that is in phase II of the human clinical trial at the Faustman lab. This treatment targets the rogue T cells that destroy the insulin producing beta cells. After doing so, new beta cells are regenerated.

A controlled hypnosis study similar to the guided-imagery study in the beginning of this chapter that enhanced white blood cell count could be carried out. Hypnotic-imagery targeting the rogue T-cells, including imagery of beta cell regeneration along with verbal suggestions and posthypnotic suggestions would be a logical approach. Weekly sessions along with an audio CD to be listened to daily and training in self-hypnosis seems like a good protocol. The beta cell regeneration has been proven. The question is, can it be emulated with hypnosis?

It has been proposed that there is a psychological component that may at least partially be part of the etiology of diabetes. Hypnosis has been suggested as a potential treatment to be used adjunct to regular treatments for both type 1 and type 2 diabetes. It is believed that hypnosis may be effective at stabilizing blood sugars and decreasing the complications associated with peripheral vascular function (Xu & Cardeña, 2007).

This makes sense, since hypnosis can affect blood flow and can also be instrumental in managing diet and exercise, which are instrumental to treating both types of diabetes.

Rheumatoid Arthritis

This inflammatory disorder usually impacts the small joints of the hands and feet. Rheumatoid arthritis is an autoimmune disorder. The immune system strikes the body's tissues, affecting the interior lining of the joints. The ensuing result may be pain and swelling, and it can lead to the deformity of the joints and bone erosion. Less often, it can impact other organs like the skin, lungs, eyes, and blood vessels. Usually occurring after forty years of age, there is no cure. Therapy is directed at symptom control and protecting the joints from damage (MayoClinic.com).

A hypnosis study of rheumatoid arthritis patients was conducted to see if hypnosis could be effective at reducing swelling, stiffness, joint pain, and the underlying autoimmune reaction. The design included twenty-six participants in the hypnosis group, twenty participants in a relaxation group, and twenty participants in a control group. Individualized hypnotic imagery was used. Subjective measures of joint pain and function were positive for hypnosis. Blood tests also supported hypnosis as effective at reducing the autoimmune reaction. Both the subjective and objective measures were even more significant for patients who practiced hypnosis imagery regularly at the follow-ups (Horton-hausknecht, Mitzdorf, & Melchart, 2000).

Alopecia

Alopecia is hair loss thought to be caused by an autoimmune disorder, not the typical baldness that many can experience. In a study of twenty-eight patients with alopecia, they were treated with hypnosis as either an adjunct treatment or only with hypnotherapy. Receiving between three and eight sessions of hypnosis proved positive for twelve of the twenty-eight patients, some of whom had a severe form of the disorder, which includes total hair loss, including eyebrows. Some of the patients had relapses, but this study does show promise for hypnotherapy in alleviating this condition (Willemsen, Vanderlinden, Deconinck, & Roseeuw, 2006).

Breast Enhancement

This hardly qualifies as healing, but since it may prevent woman from getting plastic surgery, we can consider it a form of healing. Plus, I didn't know where else to put it. Believe it or not, there are a couple of studies indicating hypnosis can help enlarge women's breasts.

A two-part experiment was done on hypnotic breast enlargement. First they tested to see if there was any change in breast size resulting from hypnosis in a small group of six women. There was none. Then they tested to see if hypnosis, which included suggestions for breast enlargement, would work in a group of thirteen women. It did (Williams J. E., 1974). Another study on breast enhancement utilized self-hypnosis.

Twenty-two women from nineteen to forty-four years old were taught self-hypnosis, including imagery. Each participant benefited with an increase in breast size. Those who were able to visualize more often saw the most increase in size (Willard, 1977).

Conclusion

The preceding compilation of studies is in no way exhaustive. The emphasis was placed on published articles in scientific journals to avoid credibility issues. As already mentioned, it is this author's opinion that case histories that have not been published, mainly due to the fact that most hypnotists don't do academic or medical research, far exceed the range of issues discussed and the depth of success written about here. As always, a certain level of maturity is expected from the reader. We are not encouraging you to discard medical treatment and choose hypnosis or other mind-body approaches instead.

In the next chapter, we will look at hypnosis and pain. This is yet another area where hypnosis is being underutilized. And as will be seen, there is no justification for its lack of use.

That which prevails, refuses to know the power of the other.
Master Po—popular 1970s TV series, *Kung Fu*

Chapter 5: Hypnosis and Pain

There are countless people who suffer on a daily basis due to pain. Unfortunately, many of these people get hooked on prescription drugs designed to reduce pain. They are often left with constant fatigue and end up with horrible addictions. This need not be so. Hypnosis is in fact extremely effective in dealing with pain. As with other areas, when it comes to pain, hypnosis should be the first line of defense, not the last.

British surgeon James Esdaile was mentioned in chapter one. He had stated that approximately 80 percent of his patients successfully used hypnosis as an anesthesia. Keep in mind these were serious surgeries, including amputations (Spiegel, 2013).

A more recent meta-analysis, a statistical study of multiple studies, revealed hypnosis to be an effective analgesia. The review of eighteen studies demonstrated hypnotic analgesia as having a moderate to large effect. This research was supportive of a broader application of hypnosis and pain management (Montgomery, DuHamel, & Redd, 2000). Randomized studies also suggest that hypnosis is not only a reliable pain management strategy, but it is also a significant one in dealing with acute and chronic pain (Patterson & Jensen, 2003).

Chronic Pain

A review of thirteen studies indicated that hypnosis compared to controls routinely had a positive impact on pain reduction for a variety of forms of chronic pain. Most of these studies utilized self-hypnosis and outperformed other approaches such as physical therapy, education, or attention (Elkins, Jensen, & Patterson, 2007). Even in cases when the intensity of pain is not reduced in a significant way with hypnosis, patients report being satisfied with hypnosis. A sense of well-being and reduced stress were among the common reports (Jensen, et al., 2006).

A controlled study dealing with participants with chronic pain in the face and mouth of unknown origin also had positive results with hypnosis. As we've seen is the case in many studies thus far, highly susceptible participants had even better results. Not discounting psychological or cognitive factors such as coping with stress, hypnosis was proven to clinically reduce pain for these participants (Abrahamsen, Baad-Hansen, & Svensson, 2008).

Fibromyalgia

Fibromyalgia is known to cause fatigue, pain that is prevalent, and causes problems processing pain. It can cause tingling and numbness in hands and feet, cognitive problems, painful menstrual cycles, memory issues, irritable bowel syndrome, and headaches. It mostly affects women as they have the disorder in a seven to one ratio with men. Approximately five million Americans have fibromyalgia (CDC.gov).

A three-group study was conducted, using a control group that received standard drug therapy. Another group received cognitive behavioral therapy A third group received cognitive behavioral therapy along with hypnotherapy. The participants in both the second group that received only cognitive behavioral therapy, and the third group that received both cognitive behavioral therapy and hypnotherapy, fared better in pain reduction than the first group that received only drugs. The third group, receiving cognitive behavioral therapy and hypnosis, fared the best in pain reduction (Castel, Salvat, Sala, &

Rull). Other research has also shown hypnosis with analgesia suggestions to be more effective than simple relaxation suggestions in reducing pain with people with fibromyalgia (Castel, Pérez, Sala, Padrol, & Rull, 2007).

Positron emission tomography (PET) was used to analyze hypnosis-induced analgesia. It revealed that hypnotic analgesia is a dynamic cerebral process. It involved multiple areas of the brain, including cortical and subcortical interaction (Wik, 1999).

It is often claimed that there is no difference between hypnotic suggestions and the regular power of suggestion. The power of suggestion, of course, is, in fact, very powerful and should never be underestimated. It is also intricately employed during hypnosis, no doubt, as are other principles and therapeutic devices. The research using a PET scan is very convincing that there is indeed a unique condition while a subject is hypnotized that amplifies that power of suggestion.

This question was investigated with fibromyalgia patients regarding their pain. Participants were hypnotized and received pain-reduction suggestions and simply given pain-reduction suggestions without being hypnotized. Participants reported greater pain reduction and control with hypnotic suggestions and also with regular suggestions. The fMRI showed that multiple areas of the brain were activated in either condition. However, certain areas of the brain had increased activity while hypnotized compared to the regular suggestion condition (Derbyshire, Whalley, & Oakley, 2009). This research seems to clearly assert that hypnotic suggestion is more powerful than regular suggestion.

Sickle Cell Anemia

Sickle cell disease is considered a genetic disorder that mostly affects Americans who are of African descent. Red blood cells are sickle shaped instead of disc shaped. These crescent-shaped cells can block blood flow in the blood vessels and can cause pain and organ damage (NIH.gov).

Hypnosis has also helped reduce pain in patients with sickle cell anemia. A very limited study of two adolescents with the disease showed that they were able to control how often and how intense the pain associated with the disease would present itself (Zeltzer, Dash, & Holland, 1979). Like fibromyalgia, the painful symptoms of this disease may be somewhat alleviated with hypnotherapy.

A larger study of various age groups also showed hypnosis as an effective therapy. An eighteen-month program that included cognitive behavioral therapy and centered on self-hypnosis showed a significant reduction in pain episodes. It is thought that the mild and moderate pain episodes were mostly eliminated, leaving only the more severe events (Dinges, et al., 1997).

Back Pain

Hypnotherapy alleviated chronic low-back pain after a brief four-session self-hypnosis treatment was used along with psychological education. Together there was a large decrease in pain. Each session saw improvement, although this study did not show a long-term benefit on later follow-ups (Tan, Fukui, Jensen, Thornby, & Waldman, 2009).

Phantom Limb

Phantom limb pain is the pain that amputees suffer from after losing a limb. Although the arm or leg no longer exists, they experience persistent pain where it once was. A small two-person study revealed hypnotherapy to be effective in treating the pain (Rosén, Willoch, Bartenstein, Berner, & R∅ sj∅ a, 2001). A PET scan revealed activity in areas of the brain associate with motor and sensory processing. The reported phantom limb pain and movement seemed in accord with brain activity.

Migraine Headaches

One review of the scientific literature considered hypnosis effective therapy for migraine headaches. It concluded that there were basically no side effects. It also met the guidelines for clinical psychology as a well-established treatment (Hammond, 2007).

A review of outpatient records of 144 children and adolescents from 1988 to 2001 produced very positive results. They were all instructed in self-hypnosis to treat their headaches. There was a substantial improvement. There was a decrease in both how often they had the migraines and of how intense they were (Kohen & Zajac, 2007).

Menopause

All women experience menopause as middle age progresses. One common symptom that many women experience is hot flashes. A recent pilot study of thirteen women who had received guided self-hypnosis recordings showed a 72 percent decrease in hot flashes and a 76 percent decrease in intensity scores (Elkins G. J., 2013).

Surgical Procedures

Participants undergoing percutaneous vascular and renal procedures assigned to three groups—one with standard care, another structured attention, and a third group receiving hypnosis—showed the level of pain increasing through the procedure for the standard care group and the structured attention group, but not the hypnosis group. All groups showed a drop in anxiety as the procedure went on. The hypnosis group well outperformed the other two groups for pain reduction and a reduction in anxiety. Hypnosis also stabilized blood flow and circulation (Lang, et al., 2000).

A small hypnosis study of twenty women getting breast biopsies yielded positive results. The design used a standard-care control group and the hypnosis group. Those who received hypnosis prior to surgery reported less pain and anxiety after surgery (Montgomery, Weltz, Seltz, & Bovbjerg, 2002).

Pediatric Cancer Patients

A study involving eighty pediatric patients with cancer had promising results reducing pain. In this case it was children between six and sixteen years of age who received regular lumbar punctures. They achieved less anxiety, pain, and behavior distress. The results with these children diminished when the switch was made from hypnosis to self-hypnosis, implying that a hypnotist may be necessary with children in this context to maintain a positive result (Liossi & Hatira, Clinical hypnosis in the alleviation of procedure-related pain in pediatric oncology patients., 2003).

Hypnosis combined with a local analgesic cream, in a random study of pediatric cancer patients of the same age range undergoing a lumbar puncture, outperformed the group using just anesthetic and the group using anesthetic and attention. They experienced less anxiety, procedural related pain, and behavioral distress while receiving the procedure. There was again a strong relationship between higher levels of hypnotic suggestibility and the intensity of benefit. For these patients, the increased effect transferred to when hypnosis was used on its own without the cream (Liossi, White, & Hatira, 2006).

Another randomized controlled study paired hypnosis against cognitive behavioral coping skills for cancer patients between the ages of five and fifteen years old. These young patients were having bone marrow removed. There was a control group, a cognitive behavioral group, and a hypnosis group in the study. Both experimental groups experienced less pain than the control, but the hypnosis group reported less anxiety and less behavioral stress than the cognitive behavioral coping group (Liossi & P., 1999). In another controlled study, hypnosis was also effective at reducing oral pain in adult cancer patients undergoing bone marrow transplants (Syrjala, Cummings, & Donaldson, 1992).

Knee Surgery

We've already mentioned hypnotic anesthesia as effective for dental surgery and restricting blood flow for a hemophiliac. There is another recent case study of a woman who had reactions to anesthetics and required a skin tumor removal on her thigh. Hypnosis was used as the only anesthetic during the surgery. During the surgery to remove the tumor from the woman's thigh, her blood pressure and heart rate did not rise. She experienced no pain and was released right after the procedure was completed (Facco, Pasquali, Zanette, & Casiglia, 2013).

A random controlled study for those undergoing knee surgeries contrasted a relaxation and guided-imagery group to a placebo group and a control group. The guided-imagery group was given ten sessions. The placebo group was given ten sessions of attention and supportive encouragement. The control group did not receive any treatment sessions. The guided-imagery relaxation group experienced reduced pain and anxiety as well as greater knee strength (Cupal & Brewer, 2001).

Traumatic Injury

A study of twenty-one patients who experienced traumatic injury and were hospitalized was conducted using virtual-reality hypnosis. Virtual-reality software and hardware were used in the experimental group and compared to a control. Less pain intensity was reported, as was less unpleasantness in relation to the control group (Patterson, Jensen, Wiechman, & Sharar, 2010).

Another virtual-reality hypnosis study focused on pain from multiple fractures received during traumatic injury. The treatment was given for two days in a row. On the third day, baseline pain was reduced from 70 percent to 30 percent, yet pain medications remained the same (Teeley, et al., 2012).

In some respects, virtual-reality hypnosis could be considered similar to an audio CD hypnotic session, just using more advanced technology and engaging the client or patient at a higher level. However, it seems more passive to me, which causes reservations. During self-hypnosis, the client actively engages their imagination. Even when listening to an audio CD hypnosis program, the client actively engages their imagination. In the traditional hypnosis session the hypnotist is facilitating the process, but the person being hypnotized participates as well. A virtual-reality simulator seems like it may have the propensity to be disempowering. Still, it is probably better than just receiving standard care.

Burns

Burn wound healing was mentioned in the last chapter. This study is focusing more on pain and anxiety. A total of twenty-three adults entering an intensive care unit in 2006 and 2007, and a control of twenty-three patients who were also entered into the intensive care unit and matched for age and sex and the surface area of the burns, were studied. The hypnosis group had reduced pain. Opioid effectiveness was enhanced. Anxiety was lessened about procedures, the number of procedures requiring anesthesia was reduced, and less skin grafting was required. The total cost per patient also dropped (Berger, et al., 2010).

Plastic Surgery

Plastic surgery requires the sometimes difficult conscious sedation of patients during surgery. A plastic surgery department conducted a retroactive investigation of hypnosis used at their practice. Hypnosis was used successfully on a regular basis to adjunct local anesthesia and was well liked by patients. Patients experienced less anxiety during and after the procedures along with more comfort. They also experienced less pain and less nausea and vomiting afterward. Overall they reported greater levels of satisfaction (Ward, Oakley, Frackowiak, & Halligan, 2003).

Still further research with patients undergoing plastic surgery showed that compared to a control using standard stress-reduction strategies, hypnosis was very effective at reducing stress, anxiety, and pain. This was despite using less medication during surgery. The hypnosis group also had more stable vital signs (Faymonville, et al., 1997).

Creating Pain

We have been looking at reducing pain with hypnosis. Hypnosis can actually create pain if desired. As crazy as that sounds, there are instances where you may have an interest in creating pain, one being in the area of research. Trying to find a cause for chronic pain in those with fibromyalgia and chronic low-back pain has caused some researchers to investigate if there may be a cause coming from a brain abnormality related to pain. Using hypnotically created pain compared to imagined pain, investigators have noted, using fMRI, that hypnotic pain showed brain activity potentially demonstrating the neural activity involved in the immediate generation of pain (Derbyshire, Whalley, Stenger, & Oakley, 2004).

Conclusion

As can be seen, hypnosis is extremely effective in pain management. If hypnosis became mainstreamed in just this one area, the amount of human suffering that would be diminished is incalculable. Again, my view is that these studies underrepresent the potency of hypnosis. Besides the reasons already mentioned, formalized studies—in an attempt to create a protocol that can be measured and objective—tend to lose a little regarding their effectiveness. The ability to tailor the session to the individual disposition and beliefs, and adapt along the way, is one of the reasons hypnosis is so effective.

As a consulting hypnotist I have personally witnessed the power of hypnosis with pain in the case of a woman who was in bed for a week due to four slipped discs in her neck and had no success with pain-killers. In this instance, one session eliminated almost all of her pain with the exception of a slight discomfort that remained deliberately due to the suggestions given. A second session a week later eliminated what was left of her pain. Afterward, a couple times over a few weeks, she was relieved—over the telephone, in a few seconds—of the slight discomfort that returned. At the time of this writing, she regularly practices self-hypnosis to improve her condition on a daily basis. This type of success among consultant hypnotists doesn't get reported, because most of them don't publish books or write in peer-reviewed journals.

Next we will look at hypnosis and the world of the mind and mental health.

Be faithful in small things because it is in them that your strength lies.
Mother Teresa

Chapter 6: Hypnosis and Mental Health

"Mind Matters"
Mental health is a growing field in general. It will continue to grow. Hypnosis will continue to grow in influence in this area, and partly as a result, the scope of practice in the mental health fields will grow to include noninvasive mind-body healing as mentioned earlier in this book. The scope and practice of hypnosis will grow as well.

Stress and Anxiety

Countless people suffer from stress and anxiety. The impact physically can be anything from sleeping problems, fatigue, digestive issues, to more serious physical problems over time. Mentally, irritability, mood swings, and depression can ensue. These can lead to poor behavioral choices from substance abuse to overeating.

Self-hypnosis is a quick and relatively inexpensive option as opposed to medications for the treatment of anxiety. It appears to work well for high-stress situations like surgery and anxiety-related disorders (Hammond, 2010). Hypnosis is also void of the potential long-term side effects and addiction posed by medications.

A controlled study over twelve weeks, using a hypnosis audio CD instead of self-hypnosis or direct hypnosis, investigated the physical and emotional aspects of occupational and life stress. Participants reported a reduction in negative self-directed statements, negative thinking, and perfectionism. They also improved eating habits. A blood test revealed a reduction of inflammatory cytokine IL-6, which is an inflammatory cytokine associated with stress (Schoen & Nowack, 2013).

Another controlled study on general stress and burnout using a hypnotic audio CD conducted for two weeks yielded positive results. The hypnotized participants were placed in several groups paired for stress level. Compared to the control group, there was a moderate to strong impact on stress and well-being. One of the hypnotized groups had a strong correlation to the level of hypnotic suggestibility and stress-reduction results, but the other did not (Cardeña, Svensson, & Hejdström, 2013).

Hypnosis also is effective at treating generalized anxiety disorder. A study of sixty participants between the ages of twenty-seven and forty-eight resulted in decreased stress and anxiety. Procrastination was also reduced (Craciun, Holdevici, & Craciun, 2012). Other research suggested that neurolinguistic programming (NLP), timeline therapy, and hypnosis all reduced the intensity of memories of stressful events (Ahmad & Zaman, 2011). It is worth pointing out here that like cognitive behavioral therapy and many other treatments, NLP and timeline therapy are often incorporated into a hypnotherapy session.

Addressing the issue of post-traumatic stress, researchers sought to determine the efficacy of hypnosis combined with cognitive behavioral therapy. The eighty-seven participants were divided into a cognitive behavioral therapy group, cognitive behavioral therapy and hypnosis treatment group, and a supportive counseling group. Hypnosis combined with cognitive behavioral therapy performed best. Both treatments produced fewer participants qualifying for post-traumatic stress disorder than did supportive counseling. The group that received cognitive behavioral therapy while hypnotized had the least number of participants with renewed experiences of post-traumatic stress disorder symptoms during the six-month follow-up (Bryant, Moulds, Guthrie, & Nixon, 2005).

A two-group study was conducted on combat-related post-traumatic stress. There was a group on antidepressants and treated with psychotherapy, and the other group was treated with hypnotherapy as an adjunct to antidepressants. The hypnotherapy group was determined to show the greatest improvement (Abramowitz, Barak, Ben-Avi, & Knobler, 2008).

One technique shown to work for people with post-traumatic stress disorder caused by combat, panic disorder, and a phobia, involves the sense of smell. While hypnotized, participants are taught to associate pleasant smells with being secure and in control. Once the smells are anchored, it can counteract the effects of the disorders just mentioned (Abramowitz & Lichtenberg, 2009).

This research demonstrates the creativity involved in hypnosis and the reason the one-size-fits-all approach of standardized studies are behind the curve regarding hypnotherapy. Unlike a drug treatment, its efficacy is often contextually driven by both hypnotherapist and patient. This treatment may work on some people and not on others. Hypnotherapy is a fluid therapy, not a rigid one.

Phobias

Another case study of a woman, fifty-five years old, involved a severe driving phobia. She also had a mobility issue. She'd had an automobile collision, but after a near accident some time later she developed a phobia. She was treated with sixteen hypnosis sessions that methodically desensitized her to driving by imagining successfully driving while hypnotized, using all of the senses. After each session, it was suggested that she practice driving with her husband in the car. She experienced a full recovery after the sixteenth session (Kraft, 2004). A case study of a woman twenty-four years of age used hypnosis, psychotherapy, and goal-oriented therapy. She had panic disorder for six months. Using this approach resulted in a recovery in six months (Kraft D. , 2012).

Another case study entailing twelve hypnosis sessions of a woman with a phobia and anxiety about flying was reported. Both the phobia and the panic-type issues were treated. This treatment also had an efficacious result (Volpe & Nash, 2012).

Claustrophobic patients may have realized one of their worst nightmares when they found that they were scheduled to have an MRI. Of the twenty participants, eighteen of them were able to be hypnotized. Of those, 90 percent, or fifteen, were able to have their MRI examination without the use of medications while in a hypnotic state (Velloso, Duprat, Martins, & Scoppetta, 2010).

Desensitization in hypnosis proved effective for blood phobia and a very sensitive gagging reflex. The gagging in this instance was preventing the use of dentures. After hypnotherapy, the patient was able to have teeth removed, and the gagging problem disappeared (Noble, 2002).

Depression

Many therapists are not trained in hypnotherapy and are not aware that hypnosis can be an effective tool to treat depression (Yapko, 2010). It was thought by many to have a negative impact on depression, but that view is starting to change. Although there is plenty of empirical evidence for hypnosis in the treatment of depression, there is a lack of research studies supporting it. Most hypnotherapists don't do research, and most researchers are educated in other therapeutic approaches.

Hypnotherapy is also very well suited for incorporating other known therapies successful at treating depression into the hypnosis session (Yapko M. D., 1993). Hypnosis can be used to initiate learning and impel new actions for the depressed person, causing new thoughts and perceptions and reducing negative generalizations and repetitive thinking (Yapko M. D., 2010).

Besides having a limited understanding of hypnosis, there are also ideological reasons for the aversion to hypnosis among many in academia and the mental health fields. They are taught a very rigid materialist belief system. Hypnosis flies in the face of that paradigm of reality.

As we have already seen, hypnosis seems to do well with mental health issues that are related to physical illness, even depression related to terminal illness (Liossi & White, 2001). Another controlled study showed hypnosis successful in treating depression, insomnia, and anxiety that was the result of tinnitus (Mirzamani, Bahrami, Moghtaderi, & Namegh, 2012). Let's take a closer look at hypnosis and depression.

There is case study evidence that hypnosis is effective with postpartum depression. This mental health issue affects 10–15 percent of women. An individually tailored hypnosis treatment was administered dealing with specific issues relative to the new mother's needs (Yexley, 2007). There is evidence that depression, both prenatal and postpartum, can have deleterious effects on a newborn child. The mother's depression affected the newborn child's biochemical balance, although prenatal depression had a greater impact (Diego, et al., 2004).

There was a controlled hypnosis experiment on chronic depression. Cognitive behavioral therapy, and hypnosis integrated with cognitive behavioral therapy, comprised the two groups in the study. Each group had significant improvement during the treatment. However, the hypnotherapy integrated with cognitive behavioral therapy group, fared significantly better (Alladin & Alibhai, 2007).

Weight Loss

In a meta-analysis of weight loss studies, cognitive behavioral therapy integrated with hypnotherapy outperformed treatment with cognitive behavioral therapy alone. This meta-analysis revealed that the people receiving cognitive behavioral therapy integrated with hypnotherapy had better results than 70 percent of the people that didn't receive hypnosis. Those classified as obese did very well with hypnosis, and long-term results were also enhanced by comparison (Kirsch, Montgomery, & Sapirstein, Hypnosis as an adjunct to cognitive-behavioral psychotherapy: a meta-analysis. 214., 1995).

Smoking Cessation

With both groups using nicotine patches, a controlled study looked at hypnotherapy and regular behavioral counseling. Each group was given two months of nicotine patches, two sixty-minute sessions, and three follow-up phone calls. At six and twelve months, the hypnotherapy group performed better than the behavioral therapy group (Carmody, et al., 2008).

Another study that did not include nicotine patches, involving twenty-one participants supported the efficacy of hypnotherapy toward smoking cessation. After three hypnotherapy sessions, 81 percent discontinued smoking. There was a 48 percent retention rate after twelve months (Elkins & Rajab, 2004). Another controlled study had twenty participants that received eight sessions of hypnotherapy over two months. Carbon monoxide testing confirmed that 40 percent stopped smoking after the therapy ended, 60 percent twelve weeks later, and at twenty-six weeks, 40 percent still maintained a smoke-free status (Elkins, Marcus, Bates, Hasan Rajab, & Cook, 2006).

Substance Addiction

One controlled study used psychotherapy for the control group and hypnotherapy for the experimental group. It yielded a more beneficial outcome for the hypnotherapy group. Compared to the psychotherapy group, more participants were able to stop the use of methadone and those who used it used less. The hypnotherapy group also experienced less discomfort and use of illegal narcotics. Of the participants who were able to withdraw from the methadone program, 94 percent were drug-free six months later (Manganiello, 1984).

Another hypnotherapy study also focused on heroin addiction in individuals who were also addicted to other illegal drugs. The patients were placed in two groups of five and engaged in group hypnosis sessions. They were treated once a week for ten weeks. One of the ten methadone patients dropped out of the program due to serious surgery. Of the rest, 100 percent stopped heroin use. They maintained this status for six months. After a two year period, seven were still heroin free, and six engaged in limited use of benzodiazepines (Kaminsky, Rosca, Budowski, Korin, & Yakhnich, 2008).

There is some clinical research indicating that intensive daily hypnotherapy sessions over the course of twenty days can be highly effective. This clinical report involves eighteen clients with substance abuse addictions treated over a seven-year period. At one-year follow-up, 77 percent were refraining from substance abuse (Potter, 2004).

There is a somewhat extraordinary case of a woman who had a very severe and expensive cocaine addiction costing her $500 a day. Apparently a very good hypnotic subject, she bought a weight loss tape and substituted the word smoking in her mind when appropriate to quit cocaine. She then listened to the tape three times and day and substituted the word coke and was able to end her addiction to cocaine (Page & Handley, 1993).

This case truly elucidates a few of the primary principles that are involved in hypnosis. She clearly was motivated. She also took advantage of the principle of repetition when she listened to it three times a day. And she wouldn't have done it if she didn't believe it would work.

Insomnia

Hypnosis has been shown to help with insomnia-caused combat-related post-traumatic stress (Abramowitz, Barak, Ben-Avi, & Knobler, 2008). Hypnosis also seems to help with cancer survivors suffering from insomnia. Self-hypnosis audio programs available on the Internet were used. The group that used the self-hypnosis program saw a slight improvement but not statistically significant, possibly due to a small sample size that was tested (Carnahan, et al., 2010). More individualized sessions would probably have better results.

There are some indications that self-hypnosis taught to children is successful at reducing sleep problems (Hawkins & Polemikos, 2002). A review of the charts of eighty-four children ages seven to seventeen years old was conducted, all of whom were taught self-hypnosis for insomnia. For the children who had problems falling asleep, 90 percent improved. Of those waking up due to aches and pain, 87 percent improved or eliminated the problem. All patients had either one or two sessions (Anbar & Slothower, 2006).

A case study of a teenage girl with type 1 diabetes experiencing sleep problems reported successful treatment with cognitive behavioral therapy integrated with hypnotherapy. In this case the importance of the sleep disorder is paramount because sleeping problems can complicate the symptoms of diabetes (Perfect & Elkins, 2010).

There was also a recent controlled study at the University of Zurich that showed that hypnosis increased slow-wave sleep by 80 percent. This study supported that the suggestion to sleep deeply was the determining factor rather than expectancy (Cordi, Schlarb, & Rasch, 2014). Slow-wave sleep aids memory and supports a healthy immune system and cell repair.

Attention Deficit Hyperactivity Disorder

A study of sixteen children with attention deficit disorder tested alert hypnosis in conjunction with neurotherapy. Beta waves were enhanced, but theta waves were inhibited. This may indicate combining the therapies is more effective and takes less time (Warner, Barabasz, & Barabasz, 2000). Other research also seems to support combining neurotherapy with alert hypnosis for treating attention deficit hyperactivity disorder (Warner, Barabasz, & Barabasz, 2000).

Conclusion

Once again hypnosis has been shown to cover a wide range of issues dealing with mental health. It often becomes gray on what is or not therapeutic, especially when dealing with mental health or habits and such. So like pain and medical issues, it is very likely that many of the less serious mental issues that consulting hypnotists deal with but that don't fall under the therapeutic label are not being reported on. Still, even of what we have just reviewed, it shows a broad range of applicability for hypnosis. I expect the use of hypnosis in this area to continue to grow.

Next we will take a peek at the unique concept of hypnopuncture. This is the combining of hypnosis with acupuncture.

Chapter 7: Hypnopuncture

Hypnosis is a very powerful adjunct to other treatments or therapies, as has already been shown. The adaptation of hypnosis toward enhancing the effect of acupuncture is an interesting concept. First we need to examine acupuncture itself, since, like hypnosis, it is often not looked on favorably, or it is dismissed out of hand without looking at the evidence in favor of it.

The professional field of acupuncture received a tremendous boost in this past decade, as researchers have empirically verified the acupuncture meridians for the first time. Popp, the world's leading researcher in the field of biophotons, and his colleagues demonstrated that after light stimulation, light channels that appear identical to the acupuncture meridians in traditional Chinese medicine appeared. Researchers concluded that a new avenue into human energy transfer has been opened and that biological life forms are not in a ground state but instead are permanently electronically excited (Schlebusch, Maric-Oehler, & Popp, 2005).

Fritz Albert Popp, who discovered biophotons—literally life lights—after years of research, was featured prominently in Lynne McTaggart's book *The Field: The Quest for the Secret Force in the Universe*. He had literally experienced professional persecution for challenging scientific dogma but was eventually vindicated. Biophotons are a form of quantum communication underlying chemical processes within and between biological systems. The amount of photon or light emission is relevant to the health of the organism. There is a balance needed with an optimum state between chaos and order (McTaggart, 2008). Some physical disorders can be from too much coherence, but many others may be from too little coherence.

McTaggart points out that this may overturn the Darwinist view of random processes fueling evolution and instead implies a feedback system of waves and frequencies driving evolution and DNA. It also may help explain limb regeneration and formation. Darwin was not the first to propose the theory of evolution. He was the first to present it with some supportive evidence and to take intelligence and divinity out of the process. Biophotons, however, acting as a communication mechanism that may drive evolutionary processes, discredit that aspect of Darwinian evolution severely. For a detailed explanation of biophotons, see the chapter titled "Beings of Light" in McTaggart's book mentioned above.

This may also explain Mesmer's animal magnetism mentioned earlier in chapter 1. Could he, in fact, have been able to intuit or feel the transfer of biophotons between him and his patients? Did he actually see these quantum light transfers in some way as a fluid that he labeled animal magnetism?

A study using electroacupuncture, which uses slight electrical stimulation to enhance the effect of regular acupuncture, was tested using fMRI regarding pain analgesia. One group received electroacupuncture, another simulated electroacupuncture, and a third group received fake electroacupuncture, meaning it was applied, but not at meridian points. The group that received the fake electroacupuncture did show changes in the brain associated with pain. However, the group that received the real electroacupuncture showed significantly more activity in the areas of the brain associated with analgesia. Thus, the increased activity in the pain neuromatrix achieved by stimulating the real meridian points, compared to the significantly less activity achieved by the stimulation of nonmeridian points, is further evidence of the validity of the acupuncture meridians and the efficacy of acupuncture toward pain (Wu, et al., 2002).

Another study using the fMRI showed that acupuncture modulated activity in the limbic system and the subcortical areas of the brain. Needles were applied to the large intestine or the hand acupuncture points. Researchers believe the modulating of the subcortical areas of the brain is a process by which acupuncture elicits its multidimensional effect on the body (Hui, et al., 2000).

Electroacupuncture has been shown in clinical studies to boost endorphins and act as an analgesic for patients with diabetic neuropathy and chronic low-back pain (Han, 2004). Acupuncture also seems to relieve pain for those with osteoarthritis in the knee when compared with a control group receiving fake acupuncture or an education control group (Berman, et al., 2004).

Combining hypnosis with acupuncture has proved very effective in the dental context. In the case of a seventy-six-year-old woman suffering from a severe gag reflex interfering with her dental care, a combination of hypnosis and acupuncture was applied. The hypnopuncture treatment proved very effective (Eitner, Wichmann, & Holst, 2005). Another case study of a fifty-year-old dental patient suffering from gag reflex was treated successfully with hypnopuncture. Five applications of hypnopuncture allowed for dental treatment (Eitner, Wichmann, & Holst, 2005).

A chronic skin condition called prurigo nodularis (PN) has very few treatment options available to alleviate the condition, and most are potentially toxic. There is a clinical case of a forty-four-year-old woman who suffered for thirty years from the disorder without relief from current treatments. Acupuncture as well as hypnosis is known to be effective at reducing itching. Not surprisingly, hypnopuncture significantly alleviated the itching, shrank the size of the lesions, and reduced their number (Samuels, Sagi, Singer, & Oberbaum, 2011).

Two more case studies of hypnopuncture demonstrated a synergistic effect. One showed hypnosis as effective at alleviating pain when applying needles to painful acupuncture points. The other showed that hypnosis may augment the effect of acupuncture in treating headaches (Samuels N. , 2005).

Hypnopuncture is another area where hypnosis can be used effectively in a synergistic manner to augment another therapy, in this case enhance the effect of acupuncture. There is a wide range of research necessary in this field. Most of the studies on acupuncture relate to pain. This may partly be due to a narrow mechanistic perspective among the medical community or just that many are unfamiliar with it. It is likely that acupuncture has a much wider area of effectiveness.

There is evidence from animal and human studies that acupuncture may have anticancer potential. It may stimulate natural killer (NK) cells, augmenting anticancer immune processes. (Johnston, Ortiz Sánchez, Vujanovic, & Li, 2011). We have already seen that hypnosis-guided imagery may do the same. Of course much more research is needed, but this may be one of many areas where hypnopuncture can be applied.

Researchers are also starting to consider hypnosis as an adjunct within the context of clinical chiropractic practice. Its effectiveness at reducing acute and chronic pain make it a valuable potential asset to chiropractic medicine. (Partington, 2009). Chiropractic manipulation under hypnotic anesthesia is also a logical area to be explored in this regard. Reducing pain, relaxing the body during manipulations, and giving suggestions that the manipulations will be successful make perfect sense.

Conclusion

The evidence in this chapter is supportive of a new treatment called hypnopuncture, which may result in further validation of both therapies and professions. There may also be greater cooperation between these two fields as a result. It may become common that acupuncturists become skilled in hypnosis to enhance their practices or regularly employ hypnotists in their practices. Logically it makes sense that in reducing pain and relaxing an individual, hypnosis would enhance acupuncture; also, it seems logical that given all the other areas of physicality in which hypnosis has been demonstrated to be an effective tool, circulating the chi, or life-force, in acupuncture seems very plausible.

At any rate, the public will be better served as both professions continue to grow in the United States and increase their visibility. After reviewing the evidence in favor of hypnopuncture in this chapter, next, in chapter 8, we will look at performance enhancement.

The visible world is created from the invisible world and is therefore influenced by the future.
David R. Hawkins, M.D., PhD

Chapter 8: Performance Enhancement

When it comes to human performance enhancement, hypnosis can assist in this area as well. Surprisingly, there is less research in this area than there is in others regarding hypnosis. We will keep our focus on published studies, as we have been doing throughout this book thus far.

Sports

Hypnosis is pretty well established to help improve sports performance. And it is not limited to the following sports either. Here are just a few examples of published studies in this field.

A study of five college basketball players was conducted to see if hypnosis could improve their game, particularly three-point scores. Imagery, triggers, and regression were all conducted during hypnosis. All participants increased mean three-point shooting scores and reported increased confidence and greater relaxation surrounding their game (Pates, Cummings, & Maynard, 2002).

A similar hypnosis study used five participants. This time, researchers focused on improving golf putting. All subjects reported more confidence, relaxation, and focus. All improved their mean putting performance (Pates, Oliver, & Maynard, 2001).

A senior European tour golf profession was the subject of another golf study involving hypnosis. The effects of this experiment were monitored over the course of eleven European tour golf events. The golfer improved his mean stroke average (Pates J. , 2013). This should actually not surprise anyone, since Tiger Woods the prominent golf professional, is said to have been trained in self-hypnosis and used these techniques since the age of thirteen to enhance his golf game.

Hypnosis has also been demonstrated to improve archery marksmanship. A case study showed marked improvement over a twenty-week hypnosis treatment. This expert archer was treated with active alert and normal hypnosis (Robazza & Bortoli, 1995).

Hypnotic-guided imagery can also help gymnasts. In this case a gymnast underperformed during competitions compared to practice. It helped her reduce anxiety and improve performance (Newmark, 2012).

Public Speaking

To address the issue of anxiety about public speaking, a study was done that had a cognitive behavioral therapy group, a cognitive behavioral therapy integrated with hypnotherapy group, and a control group. Both groups did better than the control. The hypnosis group had greater expectancies for improvement and also did improve more (Schoenberger, Kirsch, Gearan, Montgomery, & Pastyrnak, 1998).

Improving Academic Test Scores

A group hypnosis study was conducted to see if hypnosis would have an impact on college achievement tests. The study consisted of two control groups and a hypnosis group. The hypnosis group had thirty students, with one control having thirty-two students, and the other control having thirty-four students. There was a significant difference, with the hypnosis group having a higher mean score on the final test (Schreiber, 1997).

There is also research supporting that posthypnotic suggestion may improve test scores. The suggestions were designed to increase ability, relaxation, confidence, and motivation. Most test scores saw a significant improvement (Hammer, 1954).

Learning and Memory

There are quite a few studies that indicate hypnosis may actually assist in creating false memories. This in itself is an interesting phenomenon. Still, the way questions are framed can have a tremendous impact on what kind of answers you get outside of hypnosis let alone during hypnosis. An interesting study would be to ask a group open-ended or even leading questions about an event and then compare their answers to a group that is asked specific questions with controlled suggestions designed to prevent confabulations or false memories from being created. Most of the studies on memory are trying to recall memory of a prior event while the participant is in hypnosis, or they attempt to see if new information learned during hypnosis can enhance memory.

The test achievement studies above do seem to imply that future memory can be enhanced via posthypnotic suggestion. A properly designed study to test hypnotic memory enhancement should attempt to test whether a posthypnotic suggestion to accurately remember reading material being read the following day enhances memory recall while being tested afterward. I would use highly hypnotizable participants and compare them to a control group.

There is some evidence, however, that certain types of learning and memory may, in fact, be enhanced during hypnosis.

Hypnosis has been shown to improve procedural learning substantially. This relies on implicit memory. Tying your shoes or other activities that you are usually physically engaged in physically and may need to practice to memorize are types of procedural learning. It may be that hypnosis can reduce activity involving the frontal lobe attention processes, thereby enhancing procedural learning during hypnosis (Nemeth, Janacsek, Polner, & Kovacs, 2013).

Reading

This was a controlled study on students who had suffered from academic failure: low aptitude scores and some challenges with their reading ability. The hypnosis group was taught self-hypnosis. They experienced improvement in vocabulary and comprehension scores in relation to the control group. The increased vocabulary here does imply that memory was enhanced. There was a significant improvement among the participants who hypnotized themselves more often than those who did not in comprehension, reading, and vocabulary (Fillmer, 1980).

Group hypnosis conducted on behavioral-problem adolescents at a state hospital demonstrated well against a control. Sessions were conducted for ten to fifteen minutes three times a week prior to class. The hypnosis increased grade-level reading two years and three month, and the control increased by nine months (Illovsky, 1963).

A study on reading and posthypnotic suggestions for improving achievement and self-esteem was conducted. Those who were more susceptible to hypnosis scored better than those who were not. The Nelson-Denny Reading Test was administered to score reading performance (Koe & Oldridge, 1988).

Enhancing Creativity

It is believed that hypnosis can assist creativity by inhibiting critical thinking while spurring the imaginative process to explore multiple patterns of outcomes. A study with eleven participants tried this out with real-life problems. Out of the eleven subjects, ten improved on a measure of creativity, and all eleven found a solution to their problem during the four-week experiment (Sanders, 1976).

A three-group study of thirty-six men who were highly susceptible hypnotic subjects was conducted to see if hypnosis can increase creativity. The Torrance Test of Creativity was used to measure creativity. The hypnosis group scored highest. They saw a boost in overall creativity and figurative creativity; however, there was none on verbal creativity (Gur & Reyher, 1976).

A study using forty-eight participants, experiencing creative blocks in the fields of art, literature, science, or dealing with professional projects, was conducted. A control group, a waking-imagery group, a hypnotic-dream group, and a rational-discussion group were included in the study. The waking-imagery and hypnotic-dream groups reported the most positive results (Barrios & Singer, 1981).

Conclusion

Even with the somewhat limited research available in the area of performance enhancement, the published studies above do encapsulate a fairly broad scope of activities where hypnosis may be employed. It should also be evident that this is another area where "lay" hypnotists are regularly seeing success that isn't getting reported in journal articles. And some of the areas of interest are difficult to measure, like intuition, for instance.

Enslavement by illusion is comfortable; it is the liberation by Truth that people fear.
David R. Hawkins, M.D. PhD

Chapter 9: Exploring Consciousness

In this chapter we will diverge a little from the mainstream and consider some of the exciting, albeit unconventional, areas where hypnosis may have a role.

Firewalking

The phenomenon of firewalking, while not necessarily falling under the category of hypnosis, does possess some hypnotic elements that are worth mentioning. Most public firewalking seminars consist of an eight-to-ten-foot walkway about three feet wide of charred embers or wood coals. Participants will walk across these glowing red-hot coals, receiving little or no burns. The purpose of the firewalk is to assist individuals in overcoming fear and limiting beliefs. It is also a demonstration of the power of the mind.

Due to the tremendous success of firewalking seminars, some have attempted to diminish the effect claiming that it is an illusion and merely a case of a lack of conductivity of the wood fire embers. There is some truth to this; however, the criticism is not a viable explanation for why people don't get burned (Burkan, 2001).

I was fortunate enough to spend some time in Sonora, California, learning from Tolly Burkan on how to conduct a safe and effective firewalking seminar. Burkan's firewalking seminars are quite an adventure. Unlike most firewalking seminars that reach around 900 degrees, Tolly's firewalk's register between 1200 and as high as 1450 degrees on the pyrometer. The coals are glowing red, and the heat can be felt from some distance away. After three days of training, I walked across a twenty-foot firewalking pit three times on my third night. It was quite an empowering experience and certainly fulfilled the stated goals of overcoming fear and limiting beliefs.

Tolly revealed an interesting phenomenon. Oftentimes when the first person who walks across the coals gets burned and reacts badly, the rest of the firewalkers will get burned as well, to varying degrees, as they follow. Within reasonable limits, the firewalk is testing the power of belief in affecting the body's physiology. Likewise, because people have successfully walked on fire so many times, the belief that they won't get burned is a great reason why they don't get burned.

Oftentimes when firewalking seminars are conducted, people enter a group trance as they walk across the coals. This is what I would term as waking hypnosis. Many social psychologists would call it priming. A typical technique is to imagine that they are walking on cool green moss and chanting as they make it across the coals. Tolly also employs a mindfulness technique of being totally present as a method of firewalking that adds a spiritual component.

People do sometimes get burned by no fault of the seminar conductors. The conductivity of the wood does not explain the whole phenomena. It is clearly the power of belief that is the central issue of whether a firewalker gets burned or not. Since hypnosis has been shown to facilitate burn wound healing, the mind's ability through belief to reduce the likelihood of creating burn wounds shouldn't be a great intellectual leap to accept. Tolly Burkan explains firewalking and other such phenomena in his book *Extreme Spirituality*.

Psychic Abilities

We have already seen the mind's ability to change and affect matter regarding mind-body healing. In some cases this effect was even on the anatomy. Now we can take a peek at the mind's ability to affect matter that is outside of the physical body and what role hypnosis can play in that field of discovery.

This is an area of scientific research that causes disconcerting emotions among many scientists. However, beliefs and faith in those beliefs should not be allowed to interfere with scientific inquiry. While a scientist may have preconceived beliefs, those beliefs shouldn't close their minds to the possibility that truth lies outside those beliefs. To do so, they would be practicing the faith of scientism, a dogmatic adherence to orthodox views compiled by the various fields of science, not engaging in the methods of inquiry known as science.

In essence, psychic phenomenon is taking performance enhancement to a new level. There is what many consider overwhelming evidence of psychic phenomenon PSI. It may not be the dramatic parlor-trick type of effects seen on TV and in movies, but there appears to be a noticeable effect. Precognition, psychokinetic ability, and clairvoyance all have evidentiary support to varying degrees (Radin, 1997) (Radin, 2006). In Radin's books *The Conscious Universe* and *Entangled Minds,* he systematically presents the evidence for PSI and the scientific rational to support it. To disregard the evidence, statistical analysis as a whole would have to be disregarded.

In studying the effects of psychokinesis (PK), the ability to affect material objects with the mind, there is some indication that hypnosis may have a positive effect on this phenomenon. In this case, there were studies of throwing dice. Not exactly the mind-bending feats in Stephan King's classic horror novel *Carrie,* but it is a quantifiable test. While hypnotized, participants were instructed to make a certain number appear, and statistically, they had the ability to do so. Hypnosis appeared to have an effect on this phenomenon (Rhine, 1946).

A metastudy comparing PSI experiments in and out of the hypnotic state showed a significance effect on PSI (Stanford & Stein, 1994). This is evidence, to a degree, that the power of suggestion and altering or disengaging consciousness enhances PSI (Radin, 1997). Other researchers have found that by hypnotizing participants it seems to enhance PSI effects (Dubrov & Pushkin, 1982).

There is a chilling case of a French actress who was hypnotized and asked if she could see her future. She commented that she would meet an untimely and horrific death. After this revelation she was given an amnesia-induced posthypnotic suggestion. Her lack of conscious memory did not prevent her death a few months later. An accident occurred while at her hairstylist, setting her hair and clothes on fire. She was burned to death in minutes (Talbot, 1991).

Clearly the experimenters were concerned about the woman living out a self-fulfilling prophecy, which is why they erased the memory of the prophecy. The accidental nature of the bizarre death precludes that possibility, but it is possible in this case that her memory of the prophecy—if it were detailed enough—could have prevented the accident. If she knew who the hairstylist was, where it would occur, and even when, she could theoretically have avoided the horrific death. Of course, that is impossible to know.

One interesting case study was done by a physicist with a young girl. While hypnotized she was given the hypnotic suggestion that she would taste everything he did. She was blindfolded as he stood behind her, but she actually did so (Talbot, 1991). She was able to experience when the experimenter put salt in his mouth, sugar, ginger, etc.

This idea of an ESP-like connection between hypnotist and the hypnotized was capitalized even further in an interesting exploratory study of mutual hypnosis. Two highly hypnotizable participants, one male, one female, who also were trained in hypnosis, were directed to hypnotize each other, one after the other (Tart, 1967). Afterward, they experienced a shared reality that was more vivid than this world. Apparently, they were able to communicate and recall experiences in this alternate reality. This led both the researcher and the participants to conclude that it was actually different, albeit actual realities they were visiting. This prospect created uneasiness, causing them to discontinue the experiments (Talbot, 1991).

Whether or not they were actually experiencing another reality that was more vibrant or not than this reality would be difficult to prove, however, that they did experience a joint reality of a nonphysical nature, at least according to our knowledge of reality, and that the communication and or creation of this reality was nonphysical in nature, is extraordinary. Even if it were proposed that this was some kind of delusion, the fact that it was joint in nature, is what makes it an apparent phenomenon involving extrasensory perception.

Edgar Cayce, often called the sleeping prophet, lived from 1877 to 1945. Cayce may be the most extraordinary case of hypnosis and psychic ability ever recorded. At a young age, Cayce was gifted with psychic ability. As a child, it is reported that he had imaginary friends, spoke with deceased relatives, and actually remembered the contents of books while sleeping on them.

As an adult, Cayce learned to place himself in a self-induced trance, hence the name sleeping prophet. A Sunday schoolteacher, Cayce was supposedly able to access universal consciousness. This allowed him to answer questions about purpose and meaning in life, to addressing specific health issues, and the broader issues of life. In the later part of his life, to prevent people from taking advantage and using his readings for nefarious purposes, Cayce started having a third party take notes on his readings. There are actually 14,306 recorded readings that Cayce gave on over ten thousand topics. These readings fall into a few broad categories such as spiritual growth, philosophy, reincarnation, medical issues, psychic phenomenon, and dreams (EdgarCayce.org).

The *Journal of the American Medical Association* cites Cayce as the probable cause of modern day holism. His treatments were typically geared toward diet, exercise, and preventative maintenance rather than treating a specific symptoms (EdgarCayce.org). Most of these readings are specific to individual needs.

Some of Cayce's clients included US President Woodrow Wilson and inventor Thomas Edison. Some of Cayce's more controversial claims regard ancient civilizations such as Atlantis and the view that races developed separately at the same time. It isn't necessary to presume that he was correct all of the time or agree with every reading of Cayce, or even with the notion that he was tapping into universal consciousness, to accept that a self-induced hypnotic trance enhanced his psychic ability. It is possible even with a legitimate psychic that confabulations can occur without deliberate deceit. It appears that the sheer volume and apparent success of his readings, especially those regarding health and healing, indicate that he was psychic and that his trance enhanced that ability.

Another example of psychic ability being enhanced during hypnosis is the experiments done by Phineas Parkhurst Quimby in the 1840s. Quimby used a highly hypnotic subject named Lucius to assist him while treating his patients. Lucius, while in a hypnotic trance, would intuit the diagnosis of the patient's illness (Quimby, 2008). His ability seems to have been as extraordinary as Cayce's was. Quimby would hypnotize Lucius and direct Lucius to describe what the patient's ailment was. Lucius would go on and give intricate detail in his own words about what the illness or disorder was.

Quimby later determined that Lucius was either reading the thoughts of the patient or his own thoughts. Quimby eventually dispensed with Lucius and began intuiting a patient's illness by simply sitting silently with them. He was said to have not entered a hypnotic trance and simply sat with them. Quimby also began healing in this fashion as well, discarding mesmeric suggestion and engaging in silent healing, too. His technique moved from mesmerism to a purely spiritual healing method. It is one of those interesting phenomena that leave one slightly bewildered.

A common phenomenon reported in deep hypnosis is loss of body sensation, dissipation of breath awareness, total darkness, peacefulness, dissolution of ego awareness, heightened potentiality, and universal oneness (Tart, 1970). In a case study of the out-of-body phenomenon, a participant was able to state a five-digit number at a physical location lying face up on the other side of the room. It was physically impossible for her to see the number while lying in bed attached to EEG wiring. The odds of guessing a five-digit number are a hundred thousand to one (Tart, 1998). There are some recent studies that support hypnosis as a facilitator of psychic phenomenon in this regard. Hypnosis may assist extrasensory perception and out-of-body experiences in determining a target task when given specific instructions and in deep hypnotic states (Tressoldi & Del Prete, 2007).

Near Death Experiences (NDE)

While it certainly can't be proved, if preformed beliefs are withheld from the scientific method, there is very credible evidence in hundreds of case studies supporting the validity of near-death experiences (Fenwick & Fenwick, 2012), (Moody & Kubler-Ross, 2001). The hypothesis of nonexistence is not testable or verifiable in any way. It is therefore not a scientific hypothesis. Therefore, the body of evidence in support of NDEs should not be ignored. Instead, it should be examined in an open scientific manner. If that is done, we will find ourselves tilted toward the preponderance of the evidence, which clearly supports the phenomenon of the NDE.

Raymond Moody, MD, PhD, published in 1976 his groundbreaking work, in which he revealed research regarding near-death experiences involving the iconic images of the tunnel, the white light, the lifetime review, and other aspects of the phenomenon, including its name, which is now embedded in the popular culture. At the time, these images and terms were never really heard of.

Moody's work revealed the commonality of the NDE. He reviewed over 150 cases of near-death experiences. In doing so, Moody produced a compilation of common themes though a continuum of experiences that survivors of NDE's reported. In *Life After Life,* materialistic dogma is seriously challenged by the reports of unaligned individuals as they reluctantly told their stories, as reported by Moody, of what happened to them after clinical death. What Moody's book lacked in individual detail (compilations were reported to protect individual identities), it made up for it in sincerity and the reported widespread nature of the phenomenon.

Moody also does a good job revealing the cross-cultural historical traditions supporting the experiences reported on the NDE. The Greek philosopher Plato had described a similar process. So too did the *Tibetan Book of The Dead.* Emanuel Swedenborg, the eighteenth-century Swedish enlightenment scientist-turned-psychic-mystic out-of-body explorer, also reported similar accounts of life after life.

The late Elizabeth Kubler-Ross, MD, whose concept of five stages of grief are universally known, had also published research on NDEs. Ross's book is based on twenty thousand case studies. These even include blind people who were able to describe in detail the colors of jewelry and the clothing that people were wearing as well as who entered the room first while out of their bodies (Kubler-Ross, 2008).

This area of research was further explored by Dr. Peter Fenwick, a neuropsychiatrist, and his wife Elisabeth Fenwick, MA, in their book *The Truth in the Light*. Their study of over three hundred NDEs provides more detail and further develops the body of information in this field. Fenwick's background as a neuropsychiatrist creates an authoritative read as he logically discounts some of the common explanations given for the NDE. The few explanations that remain may explain away a few of the incidences, but they can't discard the great body of NDEs that are reported. Like Moody, the Fenwicks report a compilation of events that are commonly experienced by those who survive death. These events include the following: feelings of peace, out-of-body experience, the tunnel, approaching the light, the being of light, the barrier, another country or domain beyond the barrier, meeting relatives, a life review, the point of decision, the return, and the aftermath. All of these events don't happen to everybody, but most people report most of them in some variation.

Commonly, the aftermath usually severely changes them. It is often reported that there is a major advancement in consciousness. Being exposed to such an overwhelming source of love transforms the survivors. They become more compassionate and loving toward others and aware of their permanent loss of fear of death.

The Fenwicks also provide specific details and individual accounts of surviving death. Reports of hearing and seeing things that occurred while the body was clinically dead and sometimes in other rooms do lend an air of credibility. The conclusion is that these apparent NDEs may indeed be exactly what they appear to be. They may be the best documented evidence of nonphysical existence.

We've already seen that hypnosis aids the quality of life for the terminally ill. This opens another door where hypnotherapy can have a significant impact. The end stages of life are very difficult. They are painful physically and psychologically for many as they die. Hypnotherapy can provide comfort to these people taking their final steps. It may be another avenue for the dying to maintain dignity and make this final transition.

We've have also already seen that deep hypnosis induces loss of body sensation and ego attachment and produces a sense of cosmic oneness. Unlike assisted suicide with the controversy that surrounds it, and the potential for abuse due to economic incentives, the hypnotic facilitation of the natural process of leaving the body may provide a perfectly natural way of aiding the transition to the next stage of human development. Hypnosis has been shown to simulate near-death experiences to a degree (van Quekelberghe, GÃķbel, & Hertweck, 1995).

The late out-of-body explorer Robert Monroe provides comprehensive details from his experiences of the cycle of death and rebirth in his book *Far Journeys* (Monroe, 1992). Monroe had first introduced the out-of-body phenomenon to the general public in his book, *Journeys Out of The Body* in the seventies. In *Far Journeys,* he recounts his experience interacting with beings as they go through the process of incarnation and rebirth. We will take a look at this phenomenon next.

Past-Life Regression

The scientific hypothesis of reincarnation can be empirically tested and investigated, to a degree, by investigating the facts reported by those who inform us of their recall of previous lifetimes. Like NDEs, past-life experiences can be supported with evidence, but not necessarily proven. This is because it is impossible to prove that the person actually had a past life. Even if the information regarding a previous lifetime is verified, it could be attributed to a psychic phenomenon, although if evidence is found that corroborates a past-life recollection, that would indeed support the hypothesis. Even materialist astronomer Carl Sagan recognized the hypothesis of reincarnation as a legitimate scientific hypothesis (Carter, 2012). No scientific theory can be proved and can only become a more likely proposition if there is increasing evidence supporting it; however, the body of evidence in support of the proposition tilts in favor of the phenomenon, especially when considered in context with NDEs.

Swiss psychologist Carl Jung, while not speaking in the context of reincarnation, does speak of the somewhat common fantasy of young children believing their parents aren't their real parents but are caretakers (Jung, 1936). If the prospect of reincarnation were real, it would explain this. It may be that children in these cases are remembering an inkling of a prior existence.

A certain number of people who are hypnotized spontaneously go into a past-life recall with no prompting whatsoever. It is a relatively small number of people hypnotized, but significant enough to call it a common—albeit uncommon—phenomenon. In no way should it be a concern of anyone going to a hypnotist that they will have this experience, but as paranormal phenomena go, it is noteworthy. In a similar vein, a small number of those who meditate may have past-life recall.

Likewise, it is common enough as paranormal events occur, but still a very small percentage of people who meditate have this experience. Either way, in the unlikely event this happened to you, there is of course no danger to it, other than it might rattle your beliefs a little.

Most often those who experience past-life recall during hypnosis do so purposely by visiting a hypnotherapist who specializes in past-life regression. Often this is done simply for self-discovery, but often it is also done for therapeutic or healing purposes. Psychiatrist Joel Whitton, PhD, recounts many such cases in his book *Life Between Life*.

One such case involves a patient who had a hypnotically induced past-life recall of a lifetime as a Viking. While hypnotized, he began speaking a foreign language. This is a phenomenon called xenoglossy. The Canadian man was instructed during a later hypnosis session to write down some words in this past life of this foreign tongue. It turned out after independent linguists investigated the origin and veracity of the words, the words written down were of Icelandic origin and, in fact, were Old Norse. He also spoke words of Russian and Serbian or Slavic origin. If he had been a seafaring Viking traveler, this would make sense that he would know these words of places he traveled to.

In another past lifetime recalled by this patient, he was a Zoroastrian priest some thirteen hundred years earlier. In this instance while hypnotized, he wrote down a script of squiggly lines. Eventually a scholar at the Library of Congress identified the writing. Apparently it was from a dead language called Sassanid Pahlavi. This language existed in ancient Persia between 226 AD and 651 AD and is not related to present-day Iranian (Whitton & Fisher, 1987).

An interesting aspect of these cases of past-life experiences with Dr. Whitton and his patients is the reports of an in-between lifetime state. In his book he goes into some detail about the common reports among the ancient Egyptian traditions, the writings of Plato, reports from Emanuel Swedenborg, and the *Tibetan Book of the Dead*. The in-between lifetime state has some of the common themes as reported with NDEs, but it also goes into more detail about the reason for incarnations and the explanations of why certain events and circumstances happen in our lives.

In this Bardo state, as it is called by the Tibetans, there is a lifetime review similar to with NDEs, where an individual can see all that occurred in his or her lifetime in a panoramic view relatively instantly. Then it is followed by a period of rest or a period of study before another incarnation. Prior to the new incarnation, the new life is planned and negotiated. Essentially people in an effort to grow spiritually plan certain events to make up for wrongs they committed to others in prior lifetimes and to facilitate their spiritual evolution. It paints a fascinating picture, in which we are not only responsible for what happens in our lives, but we planned it. Roughly speaking, that is. The major patterns seem to be planned, but there are many events that are planned in which our choices can advance our consciousness or not. So by no means is free will not present in this notion.

This phenomenon is also reported by Brian Weiss, MD, a psychiatrist who had a patient spontaneously recall past lives during hypnosis. In this case study, which ended up as a book called *Many Lives, Many Masters,* Weiss actually spoke directly to the spiritual beings who did the lifetime review through his patient. He adds more detail to the in-between lifetime state and the beings there (Weiss, 1988).

This is an area of research that is interesting and is worthy of further investigation as an endeavor to discover more about consciousness and the nature of our existence. But whether you believe that reincarnation is real or not or the veracity of the case studies, there does appear to be a therapeutic effect. In the case study presented by Dr. Weiss, the patient was able to eliminate her panic attacks and her nightmares and other neurotic or psychological issues. In the cases reported by Dr. Whitton, the patients were able to eliminate both psychological issues and medical issues, some that were terminal.

In the same case of Dr. Whitton's already mentioned, in which the patient had spoken Old Norse and a now-dead language of ancient Persia, the patient was suffering from kidney failure. Conventional medicine was not helping him. Apparently, the hypnotic past-life regression created a therapeutic effect that brought about his healing and recovery (Whitton & Fisher, 1987).

Hypnotic past life regression is worth mentioning in the context of hypnosis mind-body healing, since Dr. Whitton had reported many cases where past-life regression was used to heal both physical and mental health issues. Dr. Weiss's case study resulted in healing many mental health issues that his patient suffered from. Naturally past lives can't become a crutch or excuse for failures of this lifetime. However, from a clinical point of view, the object is to heal the patient, and it doesn't actually matter what is real in this regard. The only thing that matters is that the patient gets well. It goes without saying that past-life regressions may not be a wise technique with many patients. This is where clinical discernment comes in to play.

There is a great amount of resistance to the idea of reincarnation in the West. When Dr. Weiss first published his book in 1988, *Many Lives, Many Masters,* he was censured by the medical establishment. He now tells how doctors e-mail him regularly on the topic as attitudes are changing. In 2010, according to Pew, 25 percent of Americans believe in reincarnation (NYTimes.com).

The poll's result is fairly consistent with a Harris poll conducted in 2003. This poll found that 27 percent of Americans believed in reincarnation. However, 40 percent of those aged twenty to twenty-nine held that belief, and only 14 percent over the age of sixty-five adhered to a belief in reincarnation. This could be due to mass media influence affecting the younger generation or less rigidity with religious doctrine. The poll also found that 90 percent of Americans believe in God, which seems a constant in the United States (WND.com).

If you were to look at Western civilization as standing on two legs, a secular Greco-Roman heritage, and a religious Judeo-Christian heritage, both of these seem to have reincarnation embedded in those roots. While the concept of reincarnation isn't necessarily mainstream in Western thought, it may be embedded in Western culture. Just about every major religion makes reference to reincarnation to some degree, and this includes Judaism and Christianity. The ancient Greeks believed in reincarnation (Rosen, 1997).

While Jewish texts don't emphasize the afterlife and focus more on worldly affairs and ethics, there are occasional references to reincarnation in their traditional scriptures. The more mystical or esoteric Jewish traditions, like Kabbalah, for example, lend more support for reincarnation. The New Testament may have several references to reincarnation as well. These include Christ himself apparently stating a belief that John the Baptist is Elijah reincarnated (Rosen, 1997). Specifically Christ's reference to Elijah reincarnating as John the Baptist appears in the Book of Matthew (Lamsa, 1985). However, it is possible that his statements were an Aramaic idiom of some kind.

We are in no way promoting a specific view on reincarnation in this chapter. There are other interpretations of the Bible statements cited above. We hope the reader is sophisticated enough to make up their own mind on the topic. The purpose for citing Biblical references is done merely to assist in removing any social taboos on the topic. When it comes to exploring this area of consciousness, hypnosis may have an important role to play.

Your mind may be the only thing that you truly own. Treat it well, and guard it well.

Joseph Sansone

Chapter 10: Mass Media Hypnosis, Placebo, Nocebo

When dealing with the issue of mass media hypnosis there is generally a pushback or resistance from people that they could be so easily influenced or manipulated. There is a reluctance to admit that their thoughts are generally not their own. There is however a simple experiment that anyone can do to verify this fact.

Simply unplug from the media matrix for one month. No TV, Internet, radio, social networks, and so on for a full month. At first there may be a feeling of loneliness in some people who are heavily media addicted. The constant stimulation in itself will be missed. Later a more peaceful state of mind will emerge.

A strange phenomenon will start happening. Going about the day, one will find that people will start talking about things that are totally unknown, and they will often speak of these current events with emotional intensity. One will still be aware of the perceived major events that occur, but the people retelling them act as intermediaries, creating an emotional buffer zone.

Even more strange, different people will start speaking using the same phrases and arguments that others will use, even though these two people may not know each other. A new phrase will be introduced to the public lexicon and will now be spoken by people as if they used it every day. It is almost as if someone is conducting a social experiment.

These people are being programmed and don't even know it. Government-controlled media often uses a specific template in order to make a large enough footprint in the consciousness of the public. This requires repetition and repackaging arguments, and more important, framing the debate. He who frames the debate wins.

The media uses a powerful and somewhat a form of group hypnosis called groupthink. This issue of conformity was tested in a famous experiment, in which a room full of people sat at a table and were asked to discern a simple issue of fact. In this case, participants consisted of several confederates and one participant who had no knowledge of the experiment. They saw a line and then three other lines of varying sizes. One of these lines obviously matched the line in question. The others did not. The confederates in the experiment purposely gave the wrong answer one after another. After the third trial, participants started going along with the group and answering incorrectly an astounding 37 percent of the time. Some participants actually questioned if they were actually seeing what they believed and had distorted perceptions. In another version of this experiment, when the participant is instructed to write their answer because they arrived late, conformity drops by two thirds. Others simply caved to social pressure and the uncomfortable feeling of standing alone. When one confederate in the group would give the correct answer, the participants dropped to only 5 percent conformity with the obviously false answer (Asch, 1956).

This study is dealing with a very simple issue of fact. Imagine the difference in conformity in something that is not quite as clear as a few lines on a wall. Opinion polls aren't used to just measure opinions; they are used to herd public opinion as well. When a polls suggests that 76 percent of the public holds a certain position, there is social pressure to conform, and many will even question if their belief can be accurate. Opinion polls are also used to erode public opinion as well. A poll that is produced showing a split in public opinion on an issue that really is at 76 percent, for example, is designed to shift opinion subtly toward a split in public opinion.

While all polls aren't designed to manipulate, many are. Under the guise of statistical analysis, which may be very useful at determining the efficacy of a drug, the subtle world of opinions and beliefs are tackled. Opinions change all the time anyway. Simply framing the question or manipulating the sample used can produce the desired results. These results are then repeated through various forms of media, using established hypnotic techniques, and the poll becomes a self-fulfilling prophecy as the public is herded.

Focus groups in the media are another form of mass media hypnosis. Here the groupthink and rules of conformity are applied as a group of people just like the viewer are all coming to an inventible conclusion on a specific issue. Identity is used in full force as the viewer can relate to members of the studio audience. Identity is a powerful hypnotic device whether used in the hypnotic state or not.

There is another powerful form of manipulation that is used. That is authority. This was tested in a famous and controversial social psychology experiment conducted on authority in the sixties (Milgram, 1963). In this experiment average people from all walks of life were recruited to participate in an experiment on obedience to authority that was camouflaged as a learning experiment. These participants were labeled as teachers. They were to read a series of questions through an intercom to a student in a nearby room. When the student, really a confederate in the experiment, answered incorrectly, that student was to be administered an electric shock by the participant teacher.

The participants were told that the experiment being conducted was to examine the use of punishment in learning. The dial was labeled with increases in shock voltage until eventually after being labeled, DANGER SEVERE SHOCK, it was labeled simply with XXX. As the experiment went on, participants got increasingly uncomfortable as the confederate student could be heard screaming in the other room with increasing electric shocks with each wrong answer. Then finally, presumably unable to respond any longer, the confederate student's lack of response was considered a wrong answer, and he was to be administered lethal the XXX voltage.

The participants, as they got uncomfortable with the instructions, were told the following four responses as necessary in sequence:

"Please continue," or "Please go on."
"The experiment requires that you continue."
"It is absolutely essential that you continue."
"You have no other choice, you must go on."

Out of the forty participants, 65 percent followed orders and went all the way to the extreme and potentially lethal electric shock. They experienced varying degrees of trauma as they did so, but they did so, nonetheless. Participants in this experiment, when troubled, looked to the experimenter for guidance and benefited from a diffusion of responsibility. These were regular people who, when pressured, obeyed authority. This does explain how easily people followed orders in the Soviet Union or Nazi Germany when they were given orders under threat of violence or worse.

Authority is regularly used in media to manipulate people. Newscasts routinely recruit experts to give an opinion designed to herd the layperson who presumably isn't such an expert. Pharmaceutical ads also have actors posing as doctors, using the authority of the medical profession to promote a drug. There is also a form of authority expressed by actors posing as survivors of various diseases.

Both Asch's study on conformity and Milgram's experiment on obedience to authority are not hypnoses experiments directly. They are experiments dealing specifically with the power of suggestion. In Asch's study, this power of suggestion comes in the form of social pressure. In Milgram's it comes in the form of authority. Some might complain that they be considered related to hypnosis. However, if we view hypnosis not only as an altered state of consciousness but also as existing on a continuum, then we need to look at priming and the power of suggestion, or waking hypnosis are part and parcel of the hypnotic phenomenon.

This is especially true regarding mass media hypnosis, where the medium has inherent hypnotic qualities. The flashing and sound cues that are employed in media are also a hypnotic trigger to keep a viewer's attention and to cue them as well. Television and movies are inherently hypnotic events; focused attention is placed on the screen and other sensory stimuli are pushed out of focus. It is accompanied by relaxation and a heightened awareness about what is focused on (Weil & Gurgevich, 2005).

Radio is another very hypnotic medium. When doing repetitive tasks like driving, people often enter a state of hypnosis. A common case would be when a driver just realized that they drove ten miles on a highway and doesn't actually remember driving the distance. Many people listen to the radio when driving. While in this altered state, listening to music, lyrics, advertisements, news, etc., there is a hypnotic effect.

When the whole media matrix in its various forms is taken together, there is a powerful mass media hypnotic effect. Mass media hypnosis is prevalent in public policy. It is also pervasive in physical and mental health. The collective beliefs in society and in media create illness. The media networks, advertisers, and the government know this.

In the same way that a constant state of fear is used to manipulate people regarding public policy, a constant state of fear is used to disempower people about their health. Collective beliefs promulgated through the media place the power on the drug to heal. These collective beliefs also place the power on genetics, diet, lifestyle, external toxins, and the diseases or disorders themselves, rather than an individual's mind or consciousness.

Identity is also used to secure the illness. Diagnosing disorders or diseases is useful for clinicians to treat common symptoms. The identification with a disease on the part of an individual is damaging to health and well-being. Once identification is established, a person can be trapped with the disease or disorder until that identification is severed. Part of the push for labeling everything under the sun as a disorder is for clinicians to get paid by insurance. The other impetus is by pharmaceutical companies to be able to trap people into the disease or disorder.

It is important to negate these belief systems when watching television or when exposed elsewhere to them. The labeling of a disease is an abstraction. It is a description of a cluster of common symptoms. It is not an actual entity that can attack a person unless they give it power to do so.

Pharmaceutical companies have become so insidious in their promotion of diseases and disorders that they use the inherently hypnotic mediums of television and radio to not only market the product and create a need, but also to create the illness. The same hypnotic visualization techniques shown to heal are used to make one ill. Images of arteries clogging up with cholesterol are shown on the television screen with verbal suggestions that certain foods will increase cholesterol. This is followed by images of the heart attack or dreadful statistics. The advertisement creates the high cholesterol by altering beliefs and using imagery while you are in a semihypnotic state and then also increases the likelihood of a heart attack.

This is called a nocebo. It is the inverse effect of a placebo. A placebo is a positive effect from a drug or treatment caused by the belief that the drug or treatment will work. The nocebo is a negative effect on health that could be caused by suggestion. This could come from a doctor or from advertisements, for example.

These same techniques are used to make the drug more effective. The imagery and suggestions are followed by imagery and suggestions that the cholesterol drug will clear the arteries and prevent heart attacks and strokes, thus creating a positive placebo effect. Even the common side effects advertised are a technique to reinforce the beliefs in the efficacy of the drug. If a person experiences mild nausea when taking the drug, this will actually help create the subconscious belief that the drug is working, and it will then work.

This is a technique used by pharmaceutical companies to breach or break the blind in double-blind studies. One study showed that 87 percent of doctors and 80 percent of patients knew they received the actual drug instead of the placebo. By guessing, the number should be around 50 percent (Sheldrake, 2012). Once patients and doctors think they are getting the actual drug in the double-blind study, then their faith and belief in the drug enhances the placebo effect, making the drug more effective than the placebo.

Sheldrake also points out that the placebo effect has been increasing in the United States, making it harder for drugs to beat the placebo in the double-blind studies. This is correlated with the extensive media campaign pumping drugs as a cure-all. Apparently, over time, antidepressants are becoming more effective in clinical trials. The media and their constant barrage of pharmaceutical ads have made them more effective (Lipton, 2008). Both the increased placebo effect in the trials and the increased efficacy of antidepressants are due to the placebo effect.

For most people diagnosed with major depressive disorder, treatment with drugs or clinical treatment does not yield much of a difference. Also, the bulk of the response to antidepressants is from the placebo. This often is a sugar pill. The kicker here is that the so-called placebo run in the clinical trial of the drug shows that the response to the placebo is the best indicator of response to the antidepressant. It is the belief and the expectation that the drug will work that causes the placebo. Hypnosis, which is integrated with both the power of suggestion and belief, is a logical treatment (Kirsch & Low, 2013).

In one study, placebos for antidepressants actually showed increased activity in the prefrontal cortex. Actual changes in brain activity were identified that were different from what would occur in the antidepressant users. This happened to the participants whom the placebo worked for (Leuchter, Cook, Witte, Morgan, & Abrams, 2002). This was even the case with long-term depression, where researchers also saw positive results and changes to the brain from the placebo.

As extraordinary as a placebo making changes to the brain may sound, it shouldn't shock us. We have already learned that hypnosis causes changes in the brain functioning and in the body's physiology, including the anatomy. We have also learned that suggestion, on its own, causes changes in the brain. These placebo studies do further illustrate that belief alters brain activity.

To understand how powerful the placebo effect is we need to consider a well-known experiment done in 2002. In a randomized controlled study involving 180 patients published in the *New England Journal of Medicine,* osteoarthritis and arthroscopy knee surgery were tested against a placebo group. One group received arthroscopic debridement, another arthroscopic lavage, and the third group received placebo surgery. This placebo group had received the skin incisions and a simulated or phony debridement. It was a twenty-four-month study, and 165 patients completed it.

To maintain the blind in the study placebo patients were given local anesthesia so they could witness the simulated debridement. The knee was manipulated and the surgeon asked for the instruments but they were never used. The clinicians even splashed around saline to simulate lavage. The time of the phony surgery was the same as a real one and the patients spent the night in recovery. All patients were given the same postoperative care, which included exercise programs and walking devices. Postoperative care also included analgesics, the use of which was similar in all three groups during the study. The blind was maintained throughout the study. The orthopedic surgeon who performed all the surgeries, including the placebo, was a doctor for an NBA basketball team at the time and was also the physician of the US Olympic basketball teams in 1996.

In both measures of pain and function, the placebo group fared as well—without a significant difference from the debridement and lavage groups—at the conclusion of the study. At some stages of follow-up, the placebo group showed better function than the debridement group (Moseley, et al., 2002).

The researchers also concluded that the placebo effect for surgeries should not be discounted, and medical professionals should always be aware of the placebo effect. This is a delicate balancing act that astute doctors need to be aware of. They need to be extremely careful, considering their position of authority, of the impact of their waking hypnosis or priming of their patients. Telling a patient that they are at risk for a disorder or disease may actually place them at risk. Patients also need to be astute. While not being in denial about medical issues, they need to internally reject negative belief systems that a doctor volunteers about their prognosis.

Conclusion

Regarding medications, in a sense, all prescribed medicines are experimental. Due to the length of the human lifespan it is not possible to understand all the long term side effects of a drug. Likewise it is even more impossible to predict the epigenetic effects a drug will have on future generations. Still, pharmacology does have a place. From a harm reduction perspective drugs can be beneficial. It is misuse and overuse that is problematic.

Placebos, nocebos, and mass media hypnosis can't be ignored. It is up to the individual to actively discern what they should self-censor from their consciousness. This includes simple things like falling asleep with the TV on. As you are dozing in and out of sleep in a semihypnotic state, you are ingesting countless commercials and viewing content into your subconscious mind. It is nearly impossible to measure the effect that these collective beliefs promoted on television and other areas of the media have on health and wellness. This applies to radio as well. We routinely enter a light state of hypnosis as we drive, and those pharmaceutical ads are running in the background.

When considering hypnotism, this is all totally relevant. If you are engaged in a hypnotic mind-body program or even a simple hypnotic weight loss program, routinely being exposed to suggestions that you are not in control of your body and are susceptible to every disease—or constantly viewing food triggers while glued to the TV—all are counterproductive to your hypnosis program.

Your mind may be the only thing that you truly own. Treat it well, and guard it well.

Part 2 Conclusion

After tracing a brief history of hypnosis, the evidence presented in section 1 of this book has been supportive of hypnosis as an altered state of consciousness that has been shown to make physiological changes in the brain. The legitimacy of the profession of hypnotism has also been supported as a unique and distinct profession.

In part 2 of this book, we've presented plenty of material evidence establishing the legitimacy of hypnosis as an adjunct and in some cases a stand-alone treatment. There should be little doubt that hypnosis is an effective approach to deal with an extremely broad spectrum of issues relating to mind or body. Equally important, there appears to be little in the way of side effects, if any.

The abundance of evidence just presented should demonstrate to the reasonable mind that hypnosis is a potent holistic healing art. From burns to bone fractures, anxiety, depression, pain, and learning, hypnosis has a role to play. Imagine if a pill existed that could be beneficial in all these areas. It would be heralded as a miracle drug. It appears that for many people, the miracle lies within. So we know that hypnosis is real, and that it works. It was necessary to demonstrate the evidence in favor of hypnosis, because this allows you as the reader to intellectually recognize its validity and subsequently begin the process of subconsciously integrating this information. This should amplify the belief that hypnosis works and as a result make hypnosis more effective if you ever decide to use it.

What do we look at next?

In part 3 of this text, we will have a little fun and speculate on why and how hypnosis and beliefs can alter biology.

Part Three

Theory and Speculation

In this section of the text we will engage in conjecture and speculation. We will attempt to adapt a few theories and concepts to mind-body phenomena. This is not an easy task in any way, shape, or form. We can't say that the originators of these theories or concepts would agree or disagree with their adaptation in the way we've presented the material. However, we feel the application of these theories is logical.

Our view is that all true science, when taken to the end, does venture into metaphysical territory. Spirituality and a spiritual perspective are embraced, rather than avoided. This in no way means we have discarded science. Science is a valuable tool. However, it is a method of inquiry that should be measured within a sound philosophical framework, which ultimately resides within a noetic context that inevitably becomes spiritual.

In part 3 of this book, science, metaphysical concepts, and spiritualty do overlap. In chapter 11 the new term and field of bioplasticity is introduced. And in chapter 12 we discuss healing fields.

I look upon the brain simply as the organ of the mind.
James Braid

Chapter 11: Bioplasticity

It is appropriate now to introduce what we believe to be a new term to our lexicon. It is the title of this book and the title of this chapter. That term is "bioplasticity." It is intended that this term will assist the process of dissembling limiting and restrictive beliefs about healing, health, and an individual's biological state of existence in general.

Bioplasticity is consciousness or the mind's ability to alter or heal the body, including the brain.

The tightest interpretation of the definition given above is limited to mind-body direct interaction or phenomena. However, a broader interpretation would also include biological changes that are deliberate results from exercise and diet, as both these activities are directed by the mind and yield physical changes. Our focus here will be on the first, tighter definition.

We have demonstrated beyond a shadow of a doubt that the mind and thought forms can and do have an impact on human physiology. The body, at least to a certain degree, is undeniably malleable at the direction of thoughts and beliefs.

Neuroplasticity is often defined as the brain's ability to change itself to adjust for injury and disease and adapt its activities responsive to new situations or environmental changes (Medterms.com). The definition of neuroplasticity promoted here is slightly different. While not discounting the generally considered definition of neuroplasticity, this perspective asserts that neuroplasticity is a subfield of bioplasticity.

In essence, the definition of neuroplasticity is not being rejected; it is just being viewed as not merely an organ of the body changing on its own in mechanical fashion to other biological or environmental stimuli. When neuroplasticity is considered within the context of bioplasticity, it is not limited to just the biological mechanisms involved in neuroplasticity, nor does it reject them, though it also includes the mind as potentially being able to cause changes on the body, which includes the brain.

This view is rejecting the empty faith that human beings are no such thing and that they are inanimate processes. It rejects the idea that human beings are nothing but biological machines acting out random processes and interactions. We accept that the mind does indeed exist. It is nonphysical in nature and is not limited to the brain.

Physician James Braid considered the brain an organ of the mind and the body as a device to communicate with the outside world in our current state of existence (Braid J. , 1843). He suggested that mind could affect matter, and matter could affect the mind. He viewed this interaction with the environment dependent on the brain's development.

He thought the soul (interchangeable with mind in this context) and the brain were unique and distinct from one another, analogous to the distinction between a musician and his musical instrument. It is well known that every molecule, cell, and particle of the human body is regularly displaced and regenerated many times in the course of human life. Braid thought that, despite this constant disposal and regeneration of the physical body over the course of a lifetime, the existence of a unique identity and memories from even early childhood was indeed evidence that the mind was extramaterial in nature.

So in his view, certain conditions of matter were needed to allow the mind to express itself in this state of existence—to oneself and to other beings. Incredibly, this position was a response to those that charged that his conception of hypnotism was an adherence to materialism. Today, most of the unscientific attacks on hypnotism are instead from those who reject it out of hand because it undermines the faith of scientism and the dogma of materialism.

Dr. Quimby, in the 1860s, spoke about a spiritual matter that surrounds and permeates every person (Quimby, 2008). Like a higher level of mind, or even beyond mind, this spiritual matter influences physical matter. Physical processes, and disturbances to physical processes, i.e., illness and disease, were a result of disturbances to this higher level of mind or spiritual matter. Quimby considered some kind of shock to this system or spiritual matter to be the impetus for disease. This shock seemed to be of an emotional nature and could be from fear or anger or even some kind of pleasure. After the initial shock, erroneous beliefs and opinions about illness or diseases were attached to and identified with.

Quimby considered these beliefs to be errors of mind. God, truth, or science, as he often called it, was beyond belief. It appears that from his perspective, healing came from a higher level of belief to correct erroneous beliefs, or it came from a state beyond belief, an apparently more formless state. Seemingly, the greater the level of truth, the less restrictive the consciousness or thought processes. He stated that thoughts were like seeds planted in an impersonal higher intelligence. Higher level thoughts or beliefs were but shadows of the truth that was beyond material or even mental form.

More recently there has been an impressive and comprehensive case presented in favor of an extended mind contained within a mind field that exists extraneously to the brain (Sheldrake,

2012). While the traditional materialistic view presents the mind as being contained in the brain or even as nonexistent, the view of an extended mind offered by Sheldrake is that of a mind field or morphic field of the mind. These mind fields, while concentrated in the brain, exist in a field that is not restricted to the brain.

This view of the mind-brain interaction is similar to how a television set works. Sheldrake explains that the brain, being a necessary component and therefore necessarily in working order to view moving images, is like a television that must have a working tube, be plugged in, and have all the components in working order to view the images. However, the images themselves are not limited to the television, and in fact, they are scrambled in the atmosphere and then descrambled as they enter the television set.

The mind field, likewise, is not limited to the brain, although a working brain is required for the mind field to express itself in this domain of existence. The mind is actually a mind field analogous to the moving images in the atmosphere that are eventually shown on the television set. The mind field, while concentrated in the brain, is not limited to the brain in this model. A radio and a radio transmitter could also be useful metaphors.

So this would mean that memories and thoughts aren't confined to the brain, but the brain is actually being directed to tune into the thought or resonate with it in a process called morphic resonance. The underlying field that gives form to the brain itself is interacting with the nonphysical field of the thought.

This provides an explanation for psychic phenomena already discussed. It is a morphic field interaction that happens through morphic resonance. The two mind fields tune in to each other's thoughts and resonate together as they exchange information.

The hypothesis of formative causation and its main theories of morphic fields and morphic resonance is not a theory limited to the mind only. It is an all-encompassing and comprehensive theory of physical reality that wraps itself around current theories in a complementary rather than competing manner. The older, though fairly reliable, Newtonian physics has proved fruitful, though less true than it once was; it necessarily must adjust to the newer empirical sciences of quantum physics, biophotonics, and cosmology. All have severely discredited the mechanistic version of the universe. Sheldrake's theory attempts to bridge the alternate realities that exist between the scientific communities. While trying to connect the old science with the newer sciences, this theory does overturn the mechanistic paradigm of reality of the older sciences and allows them to exist only within a limited context, rather than their once absolute supremacy. The fields of chemistry and biology must adapt as well.

The concepts of fixed laws of nature are discarded in favor of habits of nature. Memory is inherent in nature via morphic resonance. Morphic fields are self-resonating and resonate with similar fields, influencing each other. The effect is cumulative and habitual. The more often the pattern is followed, the more likely it will occur again. Morphic fields are probabilistic in nature. They are self-organizing wholes with spatial and temporal aspects, organizing vibrational patterns of activity. Systems influenced by morphic fields are attracted toward goals or attractors, as morphic fields give form to matter and help maintain and guide its structural and behavioral development. Creodes are the typical pathways that systems use to connect with their attractors. Morphic fields exist in hierarchies and interact with each other (Sheldrake, 2012).

Recently it has been discovered that the genetic makeup of neurons in the same brain is not identical. There is evidence that genetic changes can happen later in life and are not the result of parental inheritance. These uninherited changes may help human adaptability to changes occurring over an individual lifetime (McConnell, et al., 2013).

The implication that environmental changes could result in changes to a person's genes seemingly supports a great degree of bioplasticity. If the reaction to the environment could produce those changes, it is plausible that it is thoughts over a period of time that produces these changes. This seems supportive that nature is habitual and that, potentially, genes and DNA are as much an effect as they are a cause. As the morphic field changes as a result of new thoughts and actions over time, alterations in the field may occur, eventually altering the genes themselves.

Sheldrake handily decimates many of the pretenses of scientific orthodoxy. In his book *Science Set Free,* he presents information to undermine major tenants of materialist dogma. For example, he addresses whether nature is mechanical. He also takes on whether matter and energy are always the same and whether nature ruled by laws that are fixed or are they more like habits. He examines if matter has a consciousness and if there is a purpose to nature. He questions if there are material traces to memory and if there is nonmaterial biological inheritance. Sheldrake also looks at psychic phenomenon, alternative medicine, and if minds are contained in the brains (Sheldrake, 2012).

We know that every aspect of the physical body routinely gets destroyed and yet recreates itself. This field memory may explain how the body knows how to replicate itself. It also may explain how subatomic particles that are flickering in and out of existence each and every instant maintain the form of a body. It may also explain healing.

Morphic fields and morphic resonance may provide a suitable framework to explain hypnosis's healing effects and changes to the body's physiology and even anatomy, as well as explain why and how the alteration of beliefs can create physiological changes. Regarding the body, it may be that morphic fields are popping in and out of existence with each and every thought. It may be that only when a thought becomes a subconscious thought or belief that the morphic field becomes structurally sound. Once the field becomes structurally sound, it then alters the form and patterns of the biological system.

Looking at all the studies we have seen, it is clear that just thinking about healing isn't enough to create the healing effect. Altering heart rate and blood pressure or blood flow, boosting the immune system, or facilitating anatomical changes and bone regeneration cannot occur on a whim. It appears that it needs to become a subconscious thought first. The only other option seems to be the exact opposite state, where one is constantly in the present moment in a totally conscious state of existence all of the time, a waking meditative state were physical processes are equally altered and maintained. In this condition it may be that one is in near-total control or congruency with their morphic field, because they are one with it.

Another way to look at it would be that new attractors pop in and out of existence with every thought. That attractor only becomes viable when the thought becomes a subconscious thought or belief. Once it does, the creode or pathway for the biological pattern of activity becomes structurally sound to guide the form and its activity. The noticeable physical alteration follows.

Much of Sheldrake's emphasis is from a generational long-term evolutionary perspective. Morphic fields resonate with prior morphic fields in a kind of memory inherent in nature, according to Sheldrake's theory. That is how matter maintains its form.

Sheldrake also suggests that learning new skills is influenced by morphic resonance. Once a new behavior or skill is learned, it becomes easier for others to follow suit. The more the skill or behavior is reinforced, the easier it is for others to learn it. This leaves the door open to conscious thought being the instigator of new fields.

One thing becomes clear after studying Sheldrake's work. Biology and behavior are the same thing to a certain context. On the microlevel we call it biology; on the macrolevel we call it behavior. It makes sense that for the learning of new skills or behaviors within an organism, or for biological learning to occur, that thought must become a subconscious or unconscious belief.

Biology as a result, appears a product of belief to a great degree. Thoughts are, in fact, nonphysical. They have physical correlates in the body and brain, but a thought can't be captured and analyzed. Neurons may fire, and chemical processes may follow. They are the effect, not the initiator or cause of thoughts. Even when we use the term "thought forms," we may be referring to the newly formed morphic field and its subsequent influence.

The subconscious or unconscious mind creates a self-resonance. While the biological system's morphic fields are resonating with previous and other current similar organisms' morphic fields, these organisms, and in our discussion, human beings, are also resonating with their own prior morphic fields. The subconscious or unconscious mind may be the psychological equivalent of a morphic field, or as Quimby called it, spiritual matter.

Emile Coué had reported success at treating a wide variety of physical illness and made no qualms about the mind's power to heal the body. He described the conscious mind as being not a very reliable source for memory. The subconscious mind, he stated, is an extremely reliable device for memory. The subconscious mind controls the organs and their functions, but it can be influenced by the conscious mind (Coué, 1922).

This memory-retaining concept of the subconscious mind that has control over the health and processes of the bodily organs appears to have similar attributes as Sheldrake's morphic fields. At least regarding the individual, the subconscious mind can be viewed as either the same as an individual's morphic field, or it can possibly be looked at as an interface that, once influenced by conscious mind, can then influence the morphic field. In turn, the subconscious mind can be influenced by the morphic field and then influence the conscious mind.

Sheldrake uses the example of a flock of birds or a school of fish that can easily navigate by drawing upon the morphic field to guide their behavior. It is an almost unconscious behavior. The way his morphic resonance works is bidirectional; it is top down in the example just given, but it is also bottom up. The earlier example of when an individual of a new species learns a new skill would be a bottom-up example. He uses a classic example of lab rats that learn a new maze. Afterward, rats around the world are able to learn the maze faster due to morphic resonance.

It could be that these organisms operate more at a subconscious level than we do. If the subconscious mind is either interchangeable or an interface with morphic fields, then that could explain why limb regeneration and regeneration in general is more common among other life forms. Our cognitive development—with our expansive conscious mind and its creativity and inventiveness—could have a slight cost, in either a lessened degree of bioplasticity or a slower process of bioplasticity.

This may explain why hypnosis is so powerful at healing the body. At the direction of our conscious mind it allows us to disengage our conscious mind via the imagination and tap directly into the morphic field by way of the subconscious mind. It allows us to take control over and enhance our self-resonance.

Just as morphic fields exist in nestled hierarchies and are nonphysical, so, too, may the subconscious mind be. There may be a universal unconscious mind like Swiss psychologist Jung's collective unconscious, and within that, localized subconscious minds capable of interacting with the universal consciousness. This could be another explanation for both psychic phenomena and transcendent experiences sometimes associated with hypnosis.

Carl Jung referred to a collective unconscious that influenced an individual's psyche. He used universal unconscious interchangeably with collective unconscious, which is the term that we will use, since it is politically neutral and doesn't carry with it the potential negative stigma of collectivism. This universal unconscious may be parallel to Sheldrake's universal fields. Sheldrake also used the term collective, but we will use universal for the same reason: it is not politically charged.

As Jung studied mysticism, he realized that neurotics often had disturbances that were reflective of not an individual unconscious, but instead representative of a universal unconscious. He described it as impersonal and inherited. Jung stated that preexisting archetypes or forms existed in the universal unconscious that provided form to psychic content. These archetypes were described as instinctual. Archetypes are essentially the images of instincts or the patterns of instinctual behavior. They number equally to the number of common situations that arise in life. Archetypes are engraved in the human psyche because of the endless repetition that they have materialized throughout history. They first appear as forms without content only later to be filled with images and content. Specific situations activate certain archetypes (Jung, 1936).

Archetypes are common in literature and currently prevalent in books and movies. When an archetype is too transparent, the characters can come off as canned. Jung was very aware of the influence of archetypes on culture and society. He clearly pointed out the madness in national socialist Germany and through Europe as medieval archetypes represented themselves, influencing millions. Even the ancient Roman archetypes from two thousand years earlier were reenergized; the fasces and Roman salute were once again wielding influence. The even more ancient swastika attracted millions of soldiers to march to their deaths and commit horrible atrocities.

Generally we associate the subconscious mind with mental activity rather than biological activity. Although if we consider that biology and behavior within a certain context is in fact the same thing, and that the distinction between mind and body is in fact arbitrary, instead of being biological machines, our physicality may instead be a mental projection. The philosophical discussion is usually about material monism and dualism. Maybe mental monism should be thrown into that philosophical mix.

We don't need to take that philosophical leap to recognize that there is an inherent bioplasticity to the human body. Nor do we need to venture too far on the ledge to suggest that human bioplasticity is affected by diet, exercise, or thoughts and beliefs. Hypnosis in its various forms is the leading technique to use thoughts and alter subconscious beliefs to take advantage of human bioplasticity.

When people are engaged in mental imaging, it appears that the body can't tell the difference between the visualization and the real physical experience (Siegel, 1998). It may very well be that this is happening because the visualization is somehow pivotal to altering or creating morphic fields within the body. The imagery can be creating the new field or attractor that can be resonated with by repetition and identification with belief. While these theoretical fields are nonlocal and nonphysical in nature, at some point it does appear that energy, in a mental sense, finds its expression through thoughts and emotions and then through words and images and other sensations.

The key ingredient is belief. This is a tough concept to grasp for many, because we are talking about an intangible thing like a belief that yields tangible results on the body. The mental imagery and even verbal suggestions, while both intangible, seem a little more tangible than the concept of a belief. We can think of it as stemming from the nonmaterial origin of consciousness or awareness that then focalizes not only in time and space, but also in energy and emotion, then thoughts, and then taking form in visualizations and verbalizations. It may be that beliefs, conscious and subconscious, have different places on that assembly line. Subconscious beliefs exist closer to consciousness or awareness, and conscious beliefs exist just before the visualizations and verbal suggestions.

Bioplasticity can be looked at from a quantum physics perspective. Consciousness can be altering the physical body by collapsing the wave, according to the Heisenberg uncertainty principle. Intention and focus collapses the wave and cause subatomic particles to either materialize or become pure energy, enhancing the probability of certain outcomes (uoregon.edu). This function could be applied in context of David Bohm's more holographic model of the universe. His enfolded and unfolded universe parallels the unmanifest and manifest universe of ancient mystics, an invisible and visible universe (Bohm, 2008).

In this philosophical approach, each part of the hologram contains the whole. Such an interconnected universe would allow for a similar pattern or dynamic within the human body where each part contains the whole, or at least at the field or subatomic level. Thoughts within this human body system would potentially influence the whole system in a probabilistic manner.

To assist in adding credibility to the idea that thoughts and beliefs can alter matter, let's consider matter itself. If we were to engage in self-material reductionism and traveled inward toward the core of our physical existence, once we got past the molecular level, we'd get to the atomic level. Atoms are not the building blocks of matter as once thought. Instead they are mostly empty space. To give an idea how absurd this reality is compared to common (although inaccurate) thoughts about matter, if we were to enlarge an atom to the size of Saint Peter's Cathedral in Rome, the nucleus that contains nearly all of the mass would be the size of a grain of salt. And that nucleus is consisting of concentrated patterns of activity itself (Capra, 2010).

In his book *The Tao of Physics*, Fritjof Capra reveals the striking parallels between mysticism and the findings of modern physics. When subatomic particles are studied, they reveal a subjective universe that is probabilistic. Particles and waves are dependent on observation to determine whether they are, in fact, a particle or a wave. When matter is recognized as pulsating patterns of activity that is observer related, it becomes much easier to accept the somewhat counterintuitive idea, at least to many, that thoughts and beliefs can influence matter.

It may be that consciousness not only affects what it is observing, but it is also the substrate of existence itself. Physical objects don't have set boundaries. They interact through their field, both internally and externally. Everything is energy, vibrating at different frequencies. It is not that difficult to imagine thoughts influencing fields, influencing matter, when matter is realized to be interrelated activity, rather than static mass.

On the microlevel, matter is a condensing of the quantum field of which it is part. Ultimately the two are indistinguishable. On the macrolevel, with Einstein's general relativity, space becomes curved by the field of gravity that is caused by massive objects. However, as Capra points out, the curved space is the field itself. We are left with a situation where there is no true distinction between matter and the field, and also with a situation where the field of gravity loses its distinction from the curved space.

My simplistic conception of this is that of a room with a carpet on the floor. If the carpet is pushed toward the center, we are left with a bulge that could be considered analogous to a star in space. The surrounding area of carpet that is twisted and distorted is analogous to the space that is being bent. It may be that the space is not being curved by the gravity of a massive object. Instead it could be that the object is the result of a massive habitual condensation of the field and the ensuing patterns of activity. The distinction may be simply a matter of perspective as well.

We could also approach this topic of thoughts and fields from the chaos or nonlinear dynamics (Lorenz, 1995) perspective. Chaos patterns manifest in multiple areas at once, ranging from microscopic to the human level. They are descriptive of both dynamic order and disorder. The three general categories that chaos describes are order, disorder, and turmoil. It is the appearance of disorganization toward randomness or toward order. Strange attractors, when they appear, can foretell a sudden or rapid realignment of a system. This phase shift entails a higher probability of resonating with fields of different vibrations, causing a change to occur. It is believed that the presence of a strange attractor could enhance the proclivity for sudden leaps in evolutionary change of a system, as fields may be drawn toward different fields (Hunt, 1996).

In this perspective, thoughts and intentions could be looked at as attractors or end goals within or between fields, creating attractor fields that indirectly influence the whole physical system. In other words, it is a reshaping or altering of the organism on a nonphysical level that originates the patterns of activity that influence what appear as unrelated physical processes to casual observation.

Hunt, a UCLA researcher, believes thoughts are created from field interactions and that thoughts precede and exist within matter, leaving an imprint. Thoughts and mind permeate matter and are eternal, although they do change form. Matter is a denser level of vibration than mind. These thoughts can remain as fields that remain with forms (Hunt V. V., 1996).

It may be that thoughts arise from field interactions, creating new fields. An alignment with a field can transmit a thought, though it is likely that thoughts can in fact initiate new fields, not simply thought field interactions, but through true creative action—the initiation of a new field of reality that originates not only from a nonphysical origin, but that is not the descendant of an already existing field.

Such thoughts are not likely common; however, when they do come about they must be extremely powerful creating an extremely powerful field. We are talking about what might be called divine thought and true creativity. Whether that thought would need to be fermented into a belief and the pattern repeated to create a structurally sound field or not is unclear. Since the thought itself initiated a new field and was not the result of a field interaction, imaginably, it would immediately be accompanied by belief on all levels of consciousness and have a field that guides behavioral/biological patterns in nature without the need for repetition of habits in nature. Such a thought would come with the full package, so to speak.

This is very similar to a morphic field in biology. We may be simply looking at different ways of saying the same thing. If we looked at it in the reverse, somehow what appears physical at some point becomes more wavelike until we reach a subatomic level where we are left with clouds of probability, all of which are contained within a field. Regarding people, essentially it is some kind of field influence that alters the behavior and biology of the organism, which apparently begins with a thought or intention, or at the very least is influenced by thoughts and intentions.

Sheldrake's morphic fields, however, exist at all levels of complexity and resonate with prior fields via an inherent memory. Within them are the attractors that guide behavior. In a practical example, a person's sense of health identity, mental or physical, could be the result of such a field and operate mostly at a subconscious level, influencing physical health through another field. It may be that there are healing fields that provide the optimum state for health and well-being.

Conclusion

In this chapter we've introduced bioplasticity to the lexicon as a new context to view human mind body interaction. We've touched upon some of the new and advanced theories that may explain how the process of bioplasticity occurs. More specifically, when taken within the context of this book, we may have answers or at least potential answers to why hypnosis works for healing purposes.

Simply by throwing the term bioplasticity out there with the definition that it is consciousness or the mind's ability to alter or heal the body, including the brain, we may be facilitating creating or enhancing a powerful attractor or strengthening a powerful morphic field. If the term becomes an everyday phrase embedded in human consciousness, it will remove current limits on human healing and potential. In essence, it may be facilitating a powerful healing field, which brings us to our next chapter.

Chapter 12: Healing Fields

The nature of illness is extremely difficult to pinpoint. At least, when we continue to investigate why a disease or disorder is present, the deeper we dig, the answer is less apparent on the physical level. We can see the physical processes and the mechanics of what is going wrong, but we can't see the cause. That is because the cause is occurring with some kind of disturbance in the body's field. The physical infirmity is the result.

Thought and belief and the identification with them, and the emotional commitment to them, creates and empowers the field. This can be for positive or negative purposes relative to health. It can also be for preventative or restorative purposes.

Health is the natural expression of life and illness is often an expression of emotional pain and suffering on the physical level (Hawkins D. R., 2009). The late David R. Hawkins, MD, PhD, brings to us a unique perspective on illness in his book, *Healing and Recovery*. It is a transcription of video and audio lecture series he recorded in the eighties.

A psychiatrist with approximately fifty years of clinical experience, he had a profitable practice in New York City with many people in his employment. He left his practice and headed to Sedona for a simple life of contemplation, and years later he began teaching his spiritual perspective.

Interestingly, Hawkins reported self-healing of many documented illnesses that he had suffered from, using techniques he describes in his lectures. These illnesses ranged from allergies, hypoglycemia, high cholesterol, ulcers, and congestive heart failure, to name a few, to actually ridding himself of the need for eyeglasses after forty years of dependency.

Hawkins suggests that there are actually different levels of consciousness with their unique characteristics, some of which are detrimental to health, and others that promote health and well-being. Each level of consciousness has with it a corresponding contextual interpretation of reality and a host of potentialities that correlate with it. Meaning, purpose, and intent are therefore decided largely by the prevailing level of consciousness of an individual.

He describes a permanent awareness that is the core of one's existence. Within this field of awareness, there is consciousness, and the mind exists within that field, and finally brain and body. So the experience of the body takes place in the mind, and the experience of the mind takes place in consciousness then finally in the ultimate screen of awareness. Everything of a physical nature is actually experienced in consciousness.

To facilitate healing in a generic sense an individual needs to align themselves with higher healing fields of consciousness. It is like returning to natural state of wellness. From Hawkins's viewpoint, aligning with the higher energy fields of consciousness, such as unconditional love and forgiveness, has a therapeutic healing effect. To be connected to such a powerful attractor is often beneficial.

To illustrate the logic, beyond the alignment of the higher energy fields that we have touched on in the last chapter, we can examine how Hawkins describes the etiology or cause of most illness. He presents that most illness and disease is the result of aggravated and repressed emotions that interfere with the acupuncture meridians, coupled with specific unconscious belief systems. The interference with the acupuncture meridians creates disequilibrium in the body's natural field that interferes with the health patterns that are normally present. Over time, the illness manifests itself via the specific belief systems in the illness or disease of the body.

Realignment from negative emotions toward positive emotions is required. Of these repressed and aggravated emotions, unconscious guilt appears the biggest culprit. Moving away from judgment and condemnation facilitates this required process of forgiveness. When judgment and condemnation of others is released, internal judgments and condemnations are also relinquished. There is also a need to escape the victim-perpetrator perception of reality and the accompanying anger-guilt cycle.

Hawkins has created a stratification of the levels of consciousness corresponding to a relevant field of power. Progressively these fields increase in power in an exponential way as we approach the higher fields of consciousness. He also differentiates between power and force. These fields are influential. They are nonlinear. They are not direct. They are subtle and contextual, and they have lasting, often unseen, effects. They are representative of power in the same sense that the sun although at times hidden by the clouds and not in the forefront of thoughts has a major influence on all that occurs.

These fields are progressively life supporting. The physical is actually an expression of the field. There are corresponding emotions associated with each field. Lower fields are associated with hate and fear, for instance. Higher fields are associated with positive life-affirming emotions such as love and acceptance. The meaning, interpretation, and experience of reality are colored by the prevailing level or field of consciousness that a person is aligned with.

The identification with a particular illness is a form of self-enslavement. It empowers the field of the illness to have sway over the health of a person through the subconscious mind. This is also how collective beliefs can influence health. The belief in a certain illness has a unique field. An acceptance of that belief even on the unconscious level creates and alignment and interaction between that person's morphic field and the field of the group belief. The belief that is routinely held in mind, even if unconscious, tends to manifest. It is a practical application of the Heisenberg uncertainty principle. Intention and attention collapse the wave or particle in accordance with the belief, causing physical changes. This process is altered by the prevailing field of consciousness. It also alters the prevailing field of consciousness.

He gives an example of how such an energy field would affect an individual psychologically. We can take a look at the music entertainment industry and how it is geared toward children. Often debasing videos and music is targeted at children. What would be possibly appropriate for adults in certain circumstances is inappropriate for children and an encroachment on their innocence.

The teenage music of rebellion preys upon children in many respects. They often target preteens, too. The accompanying videos that may sometimes border on pornographic lure in children to identify with the performer. They listen to the hypnotic lyrics and repeatedly watch the videos. Over time, this identification strengthens as the subconscious absorbs the material. The child becomes entrained in this energy field that guides thoughts and behavior unknowingly for years to come.

Children get sucked in to the hypnotic imagery and music becoming entrained in that attractor field or morphic field that sets up an alignment with a certain destructive identity that indirectly guides behavior and choices. Years later, when they have outgrown the teenage years of rebellion, they are still listening to the music they heard as teenagers or are still being influenced by the field subconsciously, and the ensuing identity continues to cause problems. Kind of like the broken-window syndrome, but with an individual person, not a neighborhood.

Similarly aligning with higher energy fields, whether music or not, will have a positive life-supporting outcome dispersing its effect across an individual's psychological identity and life. The field interaction transmits information, and as resonance between the fields occurs, it benefits the individual aligning with the higher energy pattern.

Alcoholics Anonymous is another example that Dr. Hawkins gives of a higher energy healing field creating a contextual reality that facilitates the healing process. This nondenominational spiritual organization has shown extraordinary success over the years in healing alcoholism. The decentralized approach, accompanied with a nonjudging, unconditionally loving atmosphere creates a higher energy field that individuals can resonate with and align with. The surrendering to a higher power for help is also an alignment with a high energy attractor field.

An example given regarding physical health would be a three-year-old overhearing parents say that allergies and asthma runs in the family. The trusting child accepts the belief. It becomes an unconscious belief that creates a new attractor, altering the morphic field over time. This is augmented by unconscious guilt or other repressed emotions or trauma that weakens the current healthy morphic field.

When the child is eight or ten years old—or even older—they start developing allergies and start having bouts with asthma. It doesn't help that the media matrix reinforces this belief. Operating totally on an unconscious level, the trusting child experiences ill health and is unaware of any belief in the illness.

After all, the belief was adopted from the parent whom the child loves and trusts.

Excluding exposure to toxins, alignment and identification with the illness did occur at some level. True, the morphic field inherited from the parents and all prior ancestors resonates with their parents and all prior ancestors as it is stabilized. The DNA was also inherited by the same morphic resonance that gives form to the DNA. Even if that is not accepted, we do know that there is epigenetic inheritance that excludes inherited DNA. And as previously mentioned, it has now been discovered that DNA can actually change outside of the parameters of inheritance.

Regardless of DNA inheritance and the morphic resonance that occurs between child and parents—and the child's own self-resonance with their own prior fields—we know from the body of evidence presented in this book that there is a great degree of bioplasticity. Self-organizing systems, like people, may in fact maintain their form and biological/behavioral patterns due to morphic resonance; however, new biology and behavior are created when new fields arise.

This creativity or emergence of new fields can either be viewed as an alignment with already present though unmanifested fields or the creation of new fields. Either way, the new pattern offers an opportunity for a new field to be reinforced. This is true across a species: when a rat learns a new maze, it becomes possible for other rats across the world to learn that maze more quickly. It is also possible within a single self-organizing system, i.e., a person, to change their biological patterns of behavior for healing purposes. Somehow the new field gets created or emerges. When it is reinforced long enough, believed, and identified with, we see bioplasticity and a healing effect. As previously mentioned, it can happen in a negative way, too.

Often spontaneous healing occurs when a difficult or repressively emotional situation is alleviated. This could be anything from escaping a bad job or relationship to reconciling with a family member. Spontaneous healing can also occur when someone falls in love. Belief in a healing power and even acceptance of a life situation may result in spontaneous healing. In some cases, even anger directed appropriately can prompt healing (Weil, 2000).

Interrupting the pattern, releasing the restrictive field, and aligning with a new field seem the answer. Even in the case of temporary anger, if it is lifting a person up from despair or hopelessness, it may have a positive effect. However, generally anger is more often a cause, not a cure. This is probably so because the anger continues to exist unconsciously after its temporary value no longer exists. And it is a byproduct of fear, which is generally self-destructive.

It is important to emphasize something here. The bioplasticity that we see in an individual as they alter their own morphic resonance, theoretically, does not only affect them. The self-healing that one individual is capable of makes it easier for another to self-heal. The bioplasticity of an individual makes bioplasticity easier for others to do. An individual who changes their field and learns to heal from cancer creates a vibrational pattern in the field or creates a new field that others can resonate with. Like the rats running their mazes more quickly in other areas of the world because other rats have already mastered that maze, the process of learning to heal and bioplasticity in general are made easier through morphic resonance.

The publication of this book and all of the studies in it (keep in mind we've only looked at hypnosis mind-body healing) have assisted this process of morphic resonance to affirm self-healing by affirming the pattern of behavior. It positively empowers people to heal their bodies by altering their beliefs and making them aware that they too can take charge of their bodies in ways they never envisioned. The new pattern of behavior is broadcast as an attractor, and as more and more people align with that attractor and reinforce the morphic resonance of the self-healing field, the process will become easier.

Similar to Hawkins, Valerie Hunt also believes that disease or illness is an interference or disturbance with the energy field that leads to physical illness with a specific disturbance for each disease, although Hunt is speaking of electromagnetic fields. She believes that physical regeneration comes from reenergizing the body's field. New energy can improve and refine the field. To maintain a dynamic flexibility in all physical systems, the field must move toward the edge of chaos (Hunt V. V., 1996).

This is an electromagnetic view of healing. According to Hunt, bones and ligaments heal more slowly than soft tissue not only because blood and lymphatic circulation is restricted in flow compared to soft tissue, but also because the electromagnetic flow is slower and reduced as well.

Hunt proposes that basically there is an interruption in the flow of electromagnetic energy reducing its potency and narrowing the range of its vibrations. Similar to Hawkins, she suggests that a stagnation occurs when consciousness is inhibited from freely flowing though physical areas, creating illness. Like Hawkins, she suggests love has healing power. Since isolation and feelings of alienation seem to contribute to illness, she also thinks reconnecting and bonding with others in group healings has a positive field interaction that aids healing. Holistic spiritual healers in her view project an enlightened presence, thereby manifesting a stronger field to realign the field of the person being healed.

With the advent of quantum computers right around the corner, the prospect of energy healing is quite exciting. Up till now, for the most part, energy healing has only been done by spiritual healers of various sorts. Quantum and wave technologies are only used for diagnostic purposes. MRIs, ultrasounds, PET scans, and so on all are potent diagnostic tools in the medical profession. With the exception of kidney stones, where sound waves are used to break up the stones, and the recent use of transcranial magnetic stimulation, these technologies aren't being used for healing purposes.

This is probably because the government and pharmaceutical corporations are interfering with the free market. Quantum computers may make it very difficult for that pattern to continue. The medical professionals of the future in nonemergency situations may simply use advanced technology to assist individuals in resonating with their fields or get the field to resonate clearly without disturbances through quantum and wave technologies that aren't in existence yet. If there can be an electromagnetic stimulation of the brain and the creation of new patterns as there is with transcranial magnetic stimulation, then it may be possible to do that with the whole body's structure on a wavelength level of healing.

That being said, approaching it from a natural self-empowerment perspective rather than seeking external aid requires psychological and spiritual growth. According to Hawkins, the illness is there to prompt spiritual growth. The illness is a kind of wake-up call to further an individual's spiritual evolution. It is a signal prompting one to align with truth and reject the falsehood that they are currently attaching to.

It appears that when a field becomes too structurally sound, the behavioral patterns within that field become restrictive and repressive. We can see in societies and cultures that when they attach too strongly to a set of beliefs that are no longer true, a type of illness occurs in that society. Often this restriction comes in the form of oppressive collectivism, as we've seen in the twentieth century in Germany, Russia, and China. Other times it is religious rigidity, as seen in medieval times.

The dynamic quality and flexibility of a decentralized, more natural society, one of lower level or local disorder that is guided by a higher coherence, is interfered with. The cultural norms become increasingly codified into law until the necessary freedom that creates and maintains a healthy society is itself the target of attack. The continuous flow of truth into a society is rejected as the society is completely entrained in an energy field that is self-destructive. On the other side, a society can crumble because it deviates too far from a healthy field alignment and the beliefs that held it together. Many historians claimed ancient Rome declined due to a decadence and deviation from the cultural norms that built the empire.

This may be what we are looking at in an individual. If an individual is attaching to belief systems and dominant emotions that are no longer relevant or true, if they are entrained in an energy field that becomes restrictive to their own self-actualization or spiritual growth, illness manifests. Fear, guilt, or other negative emotions may have been valid temporarily, but if they are unconsciously adhered to over time, they become the equivalent of restrictive cultural norms in society that eventually become oppressive laws. They interfere with the dynamic fluidity that is required in all of nature, especially the human body. The human body and all biological systems need to be open in order to survive, but if they are too open, they will fall into disarray. A balance must be struck.

We see this anecdotally with healthy elderly people. They simply seem to be happy. They go with the flow. They don't seem too concerned with all the ills of the world and don't seem to take things too seriously. They aren't judgmental or waste their time condemning people for their faults. They haven't become rigid or restrictive in their thinking, but they also have learned to stick with what works. They have somehow managed to maintain a dynamic open attitude yet adhere to the fundamental truths they've learned over the years. Whether they know it or not, they have aligned with healing fields and have released negative emotions. They usually have a benign or loving attitude and are grateful for what they have. They haven't bought into collective beliefs in illness and have adopted empowering beliefs about themselves. They've learned to run their own race. In fact, they learned to stop racing a long time ago. The elderly who have managed to maintain their health and wellness as they age have much to teach us.

To align with higher energy healing fields there needs to be forgiveness as we need to move toward less judgment and condemnation of self and others. There needs to be an acceptance of responsibility for one's health without creating guilt. There needs to be a kind and loving attitude toward self and others. And there needs to be a letting go and surrendering to a higher power.

Thoughts come to us from the prevalent field of consciousness, but higher-level thoughts are required to create new attractors or end goals within that field. To create new fields, higher-level thoughts associated with creative imagination, are required to make that intuitive leap. Imagination is the catalyst of emerging new fields of probability. Whether we are simply aligning with already existing forms as Plato suggested, or whether creative imagination is the cause of new fields as Sheldrake says is a bit of an intellectual conundrum (Sheldrake, McKenna, & Abraham, 2001).

As the paradigm expands, ultimately we are left with a question of infinite universal consciousness or mind. A divine and infinite mind would presumably have at its disposal every possible combination imaginable. This leans toward the preexisting forms, as Plato suggests. Humans have the ability to bring into fruition new forms by aligning with them. Conversely, such an infinite divine mind would also presumably be able to create or imagine new potentialities. In this case, divine mind is simply continuing to create in the truest sense, although occasionally through a decentralized process, in this case via human beings. To play it safe, we can say that both are likely possibilities to exist either exclusively of the other or to coexist. Also, the distinction between the two could be merely semantics and a limitation of human perception. The premise that higher truth can be encapsulated in linguistics may be a very weak one.

Conclusion

In this chapter we have taken the concept of bioplasticity and looked at it from the point of view of healing fields. It has been speculated that alignment with and identification with certain fields of consciousness can either bring about healing or create illness. In part 4 of this book, we will apply these concepts to some practical basic self-hypnosis techniques and affirmative prayer.

Part 4

Practical Self-Hypnosis Strategies

In this final part of the book, a practical application of the ideas in part 3 of the text will be applied, as basic self hypnosis strategies will be looked at. In chapter 13, the yin or letting go aspect of healing is considered as is the yang or affirmative aspect of healing. Then, healing thoughts and words are considered in chapter 14. In chapter 15, self hypnosis is covered. And finally, in chapter 16, a few final thoughts on healing are discussed.

Chapter 13: The Yin and Yang of Healing

There are two aspects to healing that have been hinted at in the last two chapters. There is a yin and a yang to healing. In Eastern philosophies and spiritual traditions, the yin represents the feminine energies, those that are subtle and more contextual influences, often containing deeper meaning. The yang represents the more masculine, direct, and decisive energies. These energies are meant to be complementary. Men and women contain both energies.

The idea of aligning with healing fields is more of a yin approach, and imagination for creative healing purposes could be viewed as a yang perspective. We will take a look at both the yin and yang of healing, but first, let's take a closer look at some of the suggestions that Hawkins gives us toward healing.

Dr. Hawkins taught a very yin approach toward healing. He spoke of a mindfulness technique for healing. It entailed a constant process of surrender or letting go. It could be considered yang in the consistent nature of actively letting go, but the process itself was yin. It was very existential, based on experience, not theory. Based on his own experience of healing many illnesses and clinical observation, Hawkins states that most physical illness can be healed by the following techniques and principles (Hawkins D. R., 2012).

One premise that Hawkins proposes is that thoughts are, in fact, things and have form. This is not a new concept, nor are many of the other concepts that Hawkins elucidates. Quimby in the mid-1800s said the same thing about thoughts and had many similar ideas as the following concepts in this chapter, although he expressed them differently. Napoleon Hill's perennial best seller *Think and Grow Rich* tells us that thoughts are things, as did James Allen's *As a Man Thinketh,* and many other authors have also expounded on this concept.

This can be empirically verified to oneself though meditation and practicing mindfulness while awake. This author experienced this fact as a young child while falling asleep at night. The thoughts would be watched in the mind as they materialized. Unlike meditation where the thoughts are watched, here the thoughts were created to fall asleep.

Where these thoughts arise from, and whether they are contained in the brain or the mind is another issue. They probably arise out of the prevailing mind field and have a biological correlate that allows an individual to tune into the thought, or the biological correlate occurs when the thought is created. Either way, the thought is manifested from the nonmaterial and takes on form that gives it potency in affecting the physical system.

Hawkins also states that there needs to be a shifting in thoughts and feelings to facilitate healing, because the mind and its feelings and thoughts control the body. This has already been demonstrated with the numerous published studies recorded in this book. And we have mentioned some of the theories that may explain this phenomenon in the last couple of chapters.

He also states that what is held in mind tends to manifest in the body. This could be looked at as a practical application of quantum physics, as on a subatomic level the collapse the wave function ripples through the body. The concept was articulated in the book, *A Course in Miracles* and other mind-body self-help books. This was a book written in the 1970s that dealt with forgiveness and certain metaphysical aspects of self-healing. Quimby said essentially the same thing.

The body is merely a puppet under the direction of the mind. It is not the true self, which is nonphysical in nature. This is an important principle of self-healing, as it mentally removes a person from being at the mercy of the body. Instead, the individual becomes the causative agent.

Hawkins emphasizes that unconscious beliefs can create illness. We discussed this in the last chapter and how this can be correlated with field theories. As mentioned, no memory of the belief need exist at the conscious level.

According to Hawkins, over time repressed and suppressed emotions can initiate illness. This causes most illness. As already mentioned, it can aggravate the acupuncture meridian system and create disturbances in the field. It manifests into a form based upon the unconscious or conscious thoughts. This causes a specific illness to be chosen. The repressed or suppressed feelings can cause an infinite number of associated thoughts. The process of letting these feelings go disperses these thought forms.

This makes sense coming from a field perspective if the emotion is more closely associated with the field, even if both the emotion and the thoughts arise from the field. It is kind of like kicking out the legs from the table. The table must fall, no matter how long it has stood there. It deenergizes those thought forms.

Hawkins does suggest that rejecting the energy of and refusing certain beliefs and thoughts can be useful; however, he places much greater emphasis on letting the feeling go rather than changing thinking. This is because of the persistence of the dominant emotional states and all of their accompanying thoughts. For instance, depression can have with it all kinds of negative self-talk and imagery. Battling each thought as it arises could be tiresome, as new thoughts will replace them, giving another form to the depression emotions.

He tells us of a very Zen like technique for releasing negative emotions. It is counterintuitive to the way most people respond to any type of pain, whether it is physical or emotional. There is no resistance to the emotional feelings. Judgment and condemnation of the feeling must not be engaged in. It should be watched and observed. The individual needs to be with the feeling while letting it go. There must be a willingness to release it.

In time it will dissipate. It may be required to go deeper into it as the feelings disappear then reappear, because they may come in waves. The process of recognizing it, nonresistance, being with it, observing it, and letting it go must be continued.

As this continues, it may turn out that there is a feeling about the feeling. For instance, there may be guilt about having the feeling, a form of self-judgment because the feeling doesn't meet internalized hypothetical standards, or there could be shame for harboring the emotion. There may also be an unconscious payoff that underlies the emotion. This could be the sympathy of being the victim. Hawkins often describes it as "juicing the negative energy," almost like an addictive, secret, unconscious thrill.

There should be a focus on the physical sensations of the emotions. An individual will experience specific physical sensations for fear that may vary, depending on the degree of fear. The fear shouldn't be labeled; it should be experienced as described above. This diffuses its power, and it releases like steam being released that reduces pressure. This will diffuse energy from the thought forms. Otherwise there could be an endless array of fears that your mind will create. Attempting to address each fear is like taking a ride on an endless merry-go-round. Once one fear is addressed, then another will arise.

Ignore the thoughts and stay with letting go of the feelings and emotions and their physical sensations.

The inner self is permanent and unchangeable. Consider feelings and emotions in this context as beliefs analogous to a software program installed on a computer hard drive. The inner self or consciousness is the innocent unchangeable hard drive that merely plays the software programs installed. The key is not to identify with the feelings or emotions. They are not the self.

Persistence is required. Even when there is turmoil in life, it is necessary to keep releasing the negative emotions as they continue to manifest. This is done while practicing mindfulness, staying in the present moment, and letting the feelings go.

Keep in mind we are not talking about denial here. It is the exact opposite. Letting go is not an aversion to the feeling. That is what resisting and suppressing it are. It is releasing it by being with it, acknowledging it, and letting it run its course. It also is not expressing it, it is letting it go and surrendering it to God, or if you prefer, the universe. It is important to discern the difference here. Expressing it could equally empower the emotion as repressing it does, as you run the program again or replay the pattern.

Essentially a choice needs to be made in favor of freedom instead of slavery to the negative emotions. That there is a choice involved in emotions, especially deeper-level emotions, is alien to many people. Inner feelings can indeed be changed.

Once entrained in negative fields and their accompanying emotions, there is actually a resistance to positive emotions. There is also skepticism. In extreme cases, there are very negative people who are actually adverse to goodness. They will often immediately dislike kind people. Regarding personal well-being, it is important to welcome the positive emotional states when they come, by letting go of any resistance to them that may be the result of negative entrainment.

These positive emotions should be shared with others. It will amplify them and reinforce them as well. When negative feelings are let go, it is like relieving oneself of a heavy burden. A subtle feeling of being lighter will occur. Resonate with people who have what you want. Align with people who have healed from the same or similar issue. A beneficial field interaction will occur by associating with positive-minded people interested in healing or spiritual growth.

An individual's inner emotional state is transmitted. Others can often intuit it. The world can reflect what is held inside.

According to Hawkins, this process needs to be followed persistently. This will cause some symptoms to dissipate quickly—in days or weeks. Other conditions of a chronic nature may take months or even years. This may be because the unconscious beliefs are stronger because they have been reinforced for years. The entrainment in that specific field may be stronger because of repetition as well. Keep in mind even these are belief systems, so if dealing with multiple issues, it may surprise you which ones are vanquished quickly and which ones take a little longer. He also says that letting go of resistance to the technique itself is required. It should be done persistently through the day and then revisited at the end of the day to release any residual negativity.

It is important to stress that we should not identify with a physical disorder, to do so makes one the victim of the disorder or disease. It is also important not to label a disease. While that may serve the purpose of diagnosticians to more aptly treat their patients, it doesn't serve the individual. The labeling of a disease is an intricate belief system or program that shapes the illness.

It is not possible to feel a disease. It is an abstraction. There are only the physical sensations and their associated emotions. If there is arthritis, then the focus should be on releasing the sensations of pain in the hand. Even the label of pain needs to be released. As the physical or emotional sensations are experienced, they need to be welcomed and released, not resisted. Total focus on the sensations without labeling them is required. It is a continuous process of going deeper into it and then welcoming and releasing the sensations as they occur. As this goes on, the physical sensations will dissipate and then reappear in waves, just like emotions do, until they are gone.

It is a continuous process of moving closer to the source of thinkingness and then consciousness. It is a radical form of truth and self-acceptance. This summarizes the mindfulness-healing technique taught by Hawkins. Further exploration of these healing techniques can be read in his two books that deal specifically with healing—*Healing and Recovery* and *Letting Go: The Pathway of Surrender*.

These techniques just detailed do contain an element of self-hypnosis, in a limited, inverse way. There is the reinforcing belief that we are only subject to what we have in mind, but they mostly deal with undermining negative beliefs and are mostly bypassing beliefs with focused awareness. This can be a very effective technique.

However, this can be used effectively with self-hypnosis. The increased present-moment awareness of mindfulness and the relinquishing of repetitive negative thoughts save enormous personal thought energy. Rather than continuing to engage in endless mental exertion, the mind is freed up for positive, creative, and empowering thoughts and emotions. This gives the thought more power to energize a new attractor or create a new field. Simply put, the less a person thinks, the more powerful are their thoughts for healing and creative purposes.

The techniques described above can be employed while going about the day and in daily periods of contemplation. The contemplative period can be merged with self-hypnosis. This is one of those fine lines between meditation, affirmative prayer, and self-hypnosis. While in hypnosis, the process of experiencing, releasing, letting go, and surrendering can be enhanced. This can be accompanied with hypnotic suggestions and visualizations, if appropriate.

Really, this requires self-experimentation to see what works best. The mindfulness techniques could be done throughout the day; self-hypnosis in the mornings and or evenings could be an appropriate schedule. Or self-hypnotic suggestions could be weaved in during the day while practicing the mindfulness techniques.

Some people may lean toward the mindfulness techniques or self-hypnosis. Or alternate back and forth between the two. It is recommended that both be practiced diligently once a formula is developed that works. Each approach requires persistence, dedication, and faith in the process. Personal empowerment requires active engagement.

Affirmative self-hypnotic suggestions (waking hypnosis) conducted during the day should not be done in a robotic way. They need to be stated positively and can be done mentally. There needs to be a confidence and faith in the suggestion. There needs to be surrender to the suggestion and identification with it. Emotionally there should be an acceptance that the desired result is either already accomplished or in the process of being accomplished. The whole body should be engaged. There should also be an excitement and playfulness. In a sense, approaching it like a game is helpful.

Self-hypnotic imagery should follow the same course. It is helpful not to use the word visualize. It is better to imagine or pretend, because people can sometimes get hung up with visualizations and sabotage themselves by thinking that they can't visualize. Everybody can imagine or pretend, and by doing so, they not only visualize, but they also engage all the other senses.

If for example, you have injured your arm and are attempting to accelerate the healing process, a simple approach could be as follows. The yin approach would be to not resist the pain, to welcome it, and to continually release it to God, while in the present moment. While continuing this process of letting go through the day, the self-hypnotic suggestion that your arm is healing or that you are healthy could be done, while simultaneously imagining that white light is permeating the arm, healing it, and regenerating it, and imagining the arm as healthy. Just as you surrender the pain or symptoms, conversely you also need to surrender to the self-hypnotic suggestions and self-hypnotic imagery. It requires total commitment.

Play around with how often to do the waking hypnosis suggestions and imagery during the day. It needs to be frequent enough to be a dominant thought, but it can't end up being a chore either. It can be done anywhere from twice an hour or more, to a few times a day.

Likewise, periods of twenty or more minutes in the morning and in the evening could be used to sit quietly in a self-hypnotic state. In this altered state, the pain is welcomed and released—as you continue to move more deeply into the pain or pressure without labeling it—and then surrendering it to God. The self-hypnotic suggestion is given periodically, and appropriate visualizations are done while simultaneously continuing the letting go process.

Conclusion

What has been discussed in this chapter are deceptively simple, yet extremely effective techniques for healing. They do require a certain amount of self-discipline and commitment but are worth the effort.

Chapter 14: Healing Thoughts and Words

Unfortunately, we can't come up with an accurate estimate of the average number of daily repetitive thoughts a person has in a day. This appears to be because there is no accurate way of measuring them. Estimates range from a couple thousand to close to a hundred thousand a day. These are really still guesses, though.

Anybody who has ever meditated knows that the number of daily thoughts is a lot, where ever it falls on the guesstimates scale. This is because most thoughts are just below the conscious screen of awareness. We've all experienced intrusive annoying thoughts to some degree, but the thoughts that are unnoticed may be more destructive, because we are unaware of the damage they do.

When meditating and practicing watchfulness, these thoughts become discovered. It also becomes clear that they are mostly not our own but are stemming from a relevant field of consciousness, or the subconscious mind. The more watchful we become, the less energized these thoughts become. Eventually we can intercept them by placing our focus on their formation, which stems from an emotional or energy field. The adept meditators place themselves just before the thought formation and stay there. The mindfulness technique mentioned can be used to intercept and deenergize these thoughts. This yin approach should be incorporated with the yang approach, as already stated. Let's take a closer look at the yang or affirmative approach of waking self-hypnotic suggestions.

First we need to consider the subconscious mind and its characteristics in more detail. When we consider the conscious mind and the subconscious mind, they should be considered different aspects of the same whole. They are complementary rather than in competition.

Each is influenced by the other, however. The repetitive habitual thoughts that occur on a daily basis certainly have an influence on conscious thoughts, attitudes, and emotions. Their influence, as a result, also has a physical effect.

Conversely, the conscious mind has an effect on the subconscious mind, and actually when asserted, it is the dominant of the two. It is the conscious decisions regularly chosen that create the habitual thoughts that get reflected from the subconscious mind. The conscious mind is the part of mind that is in the forefront of awareness. It is the captain of the subconscious mind, which acts as a loyal crew, albeit an infinitely powerful and seemingly limitless crew.

The subconscious is kind of a reservoir that contains every thought and image. It can also interpret the body's status. This was demonstrated in the case mentioned earlier, where corneal transplants were being rejected. Finally, through hypnosis, the transplant was attempted when the subconscious mind stated the body was ready for the transplant.

The subconscious mind also has access to other fields of consciousness. This has been demonstrated by the apparent increased psychic ability during hypnosis. It appears that the subconscious mind may be an interface to creative intelligence or infinite intelligence. Many creative people rely on their subconscious minds to get specific answers to their questions. Apparently, the man that is considered to be the father of organic chemistry was revealed the structure of molecules in a dream (Hawkins D. R., 2002). Likewise, inventors such as Thomas Edison have relied heavily on their subconscious minds for the creativity that they eventually bring to reality (Hill, 1987).

All of the bodily functions are regulated by the subconscious mind. The heartbeat and chemical and hormonal interactions, including all of the autonomic physical actions, fall under the domain of the subconscious mind. This includes breathing. Deep meditators and yoga adepts have changed heart rate and other physical actions (Danucalov, Simoes, Kozasa, & Leite, 2008). In chilled forty-degree temperatures, Tibetan Monks can produce steam as their body temperature heats wet sheets thrown over them (Cromie, 2002). This is a case of heightened present-moment awareness altering typically subconsciously controlled activities. The purpose of the meditation isn't to create this effect. The effect is a byproduct of the deep meditation.

Breathing is a subconsciously controlled activity that anybody can quickly take conscious control over. While we sleep, the subconscious mind sees to all the bodily functions, including breathing. We can easily enough take control over this activity while waking. Simply relaxing and doing slow, rhythmic breathing is an example of this.

The subconscious mind is quite literal. It will reflect what the conscious mind feeds it. It is like a fertile field where the conscious mind can plant the seeds of thoughts. The more the seeds are planted, the greater the likelihood of those thoughts growing to fruition in the subconscious mind.

For the purposes of healing, these conscious thoughts need to become subconscious beliefs. Then these subconscious beliefs will become habitual and no longer will need conscious direction. Many people, unfortunately, have either been programmed by others, especially when young, or they have reacted to external situations negatively, and they have programmed themselves negatively. As a result they are guided by negative subconscious influences.

As already mentioned excessive repetitive negative thoughts interfere with the body's autonomic functions by interfering with the body's acupuncture system or energy field that corresponds to the subconscious mind. It is therefore necessary to become more watchful of thoughts and presumptions.

Generally speaking, the mind can only be occupied by one conscious thought at a time. This is an important concept that can be used to correct thought patterns and their emotional correlates that wreak havoc on physical or mental health. It is wise to never finish a negative thought and to immediately counter it with a positive thought that may often be the exact opposite thought.

The subconscious mind will absorb every thought you plant in it. To alter negative thoughts we need to interrupt the current pattern of thoughts and replace them with positive thoughts and images. This will likely take a little time. A swiftly moving cruise ship can't make a 180-degree turn on an instant. If it did so it would capsize. The subconscious mind may not capsize, but it may also need time to reverse course. All of the previous seeds of thought that have been unconsciously planted need to be counterbalanced with the new seeds of thought. If we are dealing with firmly implanted unconscious beliefs, then it may take time and effort to see the effective change.

All of the thoughts and events that have contributed to the subconscious beliefs have resulted in the physical reality that we are experiencing. The repetitive thoughts arising out of the emotional fields of fear, anxiety, hopelessness, anger, worry, and so on need to be altered. This can be done, but it needs to be done consistently.

Fortunately, the subconscious mind does not reason or argue. Just as it has been programmed or planted with negative thoughts, it too can be planted with positive thoughts. The power to plant the seeds resides with the conscious mind. The ability to access creative intelligence or infinite intelligence is granted through the subconscious aspect of the mind at the direction of the conscious mind. This creative power can be harnessed for positive, healthy purposes.

Mastering the interaction between the conscious and subconscious mind is a vital key to well-being. Eventually what is planted in the subconscious will be expressed consciously or physically. We often engage consciously in negative thinking that interferes with good health. Keeping in mind that we are speaking about two aspects of the same whole, our focus needs to be on the conscious mind, by habitually thinking empowering thoughts that will eventually be fortified as subconscious beliefs, which will create new and positive habitual subconscious thoughts that will have physical correlates.

Dr. Phineas Parkhurst Quimby in the mid-1800s also stated that faulty beliefs were the cause of illness. Illness was error. The beliefs in the disease itself were the error. Quimby was very critical of many of the physicians of his day for promoting a false belief in illness and disease. Quimby also took the position that all medical treatment was dependent on the patient's belief, and it acted through the patient's mind (Quimby, 2008).

It is important to never give credence to external phenomenon over your health. Giving power to the outside world is a relinquishing of the power to heal and control one's health. The power that resides within and heals a cut is the same power that can restore the body toward health. There must be a dedicated faith in this process and power. The subconscious mind is an interface to tap into the inherent life force within.

Part of this power resides in the language we use on a daily basis. Be as watchful of the words spoken as of the internal thoughts that float by the screen of consciousness. Our language often reveals our fears and limiting beliefs. Our words can greatly influence our emotional states. Our words also affect general attitudes and perpetuate the belief structure that underlies our thought processes.

A limited vocabulary can actually create, or at least perpetuate, a limited range of thoughts, emotions, and beliefs. Altering the regular use of disempowering words and vocabulary to those that are positive can have a transformative effect. We can either enhance or diffuse our emotional intensity with the words we speak and their accompanying metaphors. We need to pay attention to the adjectives and adverbs used and make sure their emotional intensity serves us, and whether they are emotional enhancers or emotional diffusers.

A tip in this area would be to shift toward using words and phrases that give the creative power of experience to us and not to the external world. Certainly all self-identifying statements that are negative and belittling need to be interrupted and replaced with positive and empowering words.

Within every question there is an inherent answer. The question sets up the paradigm or field of consciousness. The questions that we routinely ask ourselves, whether out loud or simply just as an internal thought, need to be scrutinized as well. Shifting these internal questions expands the contextual field and creates a leap into a higher domain of reality.

Self-defeating questions like "Why does this always happen to me?" or "What did I do to deserve this?" will produce a host of explanations telling us why. The subconscious mind will answer the question that the conscious mind asks it. It serves us to ask better questions then. For example, "What can I learn from this?" or "How can this lead to a better place?" will prompt the subconscious mind to produce better answers. Remember, the questions we plant in the subconscious will reap and produce answers whether they serve us or not.

When we start interrupting the pattern of internal thoughts and words with positive self-hypnotic suggestions, this process needs to be done with total faith. Repetition will serve this process, but the process of self-hypnotic suggestions is not robotic repetition of a statement. We need to engage our body, mind, and spirit.

Ideally the self-hypnosis regimen would entail twenty-minute (or more) sessions in the morning and the evenings—if there is only time for once a day, that is fine—after which, thoughts should be directed elsewhere. This should be accompanied by a protocol of waking self-hypnotic suggestions and images that could be conducted once or twice an hour during the day, for instance. And then little thought should be given to the healing in the intervals. Besides the waking self-hypnotic suggestions, min iself-hypnosis sessions could be conducted for five or more minutes if there is time, periodically.

These aren't hard and set rules by any stretch; they are loose guidelines on how long and how often to engage in self-hypnosis. Self-experimentation is always recommended. Some people may benefit from more constant reinforcement, but others might not.

In contrast to self-hypnotic suggestions that are planted in the subconscious mind and then attention directed elsewhere, the negation of negative thoughts and replacing them with their positive opposite should be done whenever they are discovered. This also applies to limiting beliefs or beliefs about illness that give power to the external world. The belief that eggs cause high cholesterol or that a certain food will cause indigestion needs to be negated on the spot, as do similar suggestions coming from the television or radio. This also applies to your doctor. We can follow sound advice from a doctor about healthy practices while also silently negating their well-meaning negative waking hypnotic suggestions. Remember, we place a certain amount of authority in what our doctors say. We need to remove that authority from them and reclaim it for ourselves.

This doesn't mean we should disregard sound medical advice or be in denial about a medical condition. The process of empowerment through self-hypnosis will make the treatments more effective.

The most effective self-hypnotic suggestions are in the form of affirmative prayer. We are tapping into the Creative Intelligence within. The subconscious mind is an interface with this Infinite Intelligence. Potentially the subconscious mind is a way to tap into the storehouse of Universal Consciousness. This is why, when asked the proper questions, it will produce the right answer.

An effective way to do this is to call upon God's healing presence to fill us. With total faith in the process, we use imagery and words that are of a healing nature. And we express gratitude as if the result is already done.

For example a general self-hypnotic affirmative prayer could be as follows:

> By the Grace of God, I am filled with the light of Divinity. God's healing presence fills me. The life-force is permeating every fiber and every cell of my body, healing my body at all levels. On a subatomic level, I am being healed. My subconscious mind is actively restoring my body to perfect health now.

As already stated this is to be done with gratitude as if the healing has already occurred. Imagining the inner light of divinity or the Holy Spirit within and around the body while in this self-hypnotic state should be done as well. Of course, this is a generic affirmative prayer. Like everything else with self-hypnosis, it should be tailored to individual beliefs and preferences.

Again, there are no hard set rules here. If specific religious imagery increases faith, then by all means, invoke it. The key ingredients are in a state of faith, invoking divinity, using the power of the subconscious mind, positive self-hypnotic suggestions and imagery, and gratitude for the healing as if it has already happened. And of course repeating the process until it is accepted as a subconscious belief. A total surrendering to the process is required.

We can also be more specific with the suggestions and target appropriate body parts or organs. We can also imagine those specific organs or body parts as if they are healed. Bathe them in light of any color and so on. We can also imagine getting a healing injection or other types of imagery and verbal suggestions.

It is important to create a mental image of wellness and to create an emotional union with that future reality as if it were already existent. This creates an attractor within the morphic field of your subconscious mind. We need to identify with this reality, not the present illness.

It is worth pointing out that self-hypnosis and or affirmative prayer is beneficial to the healthy person as well as those that are ill. Constantly casting a field of reality in the subconscious mind of wellness and vitality will act as a form of preventative medicine. In a probabilistic universe, the patterned behavior or unconscious biological processes will follow the creode of health that you create. A twenty-minute session once a day is the mental version of an apple a day keeping the doctor away.

We need to become our own Asklipian physician priests. We need to break down the resistance to health and affirm it at the same time. It is also wise to practice these techniques while drifting off to sleep at night. Doing so will guide the subconscious mind as we sleep. The same subconscious mind that ensures that we breathe while we are asleep and maintains all of the bodily processes, also sees to the mind's activities as well. This is a fertile time to plant seeds of wellness.

When just waking in the morning and still lying in bed in a semi awake state, it is also beneficial to practice these self-hypnosis techniques. Doing so will act as a guide for your subconscious mind throughout the day. This establishes a field of wellness that will help guide your thoughts during the day.

The yin techniques for healing discussed earlier remove the conscious barriers toward health. Doing so allows the natural state of well-being to be restored. The more yang approach of self-hypnosis accomplishes the same thing, but from a different angle. While in a state of hypnosis, the resistance from the conscious mind is dramatically reduced, if not eliminated. This is probably why there have been cases of people healing just by entering a deep state of hypnosis. In this altered state, where the resistance of the conscious mind is eliminated, affirmative self-hypnotic suggestions simply assist and accelerate the process of restoration.

Together, the yin and yang of mindfulness and self-hypnosis is a potent mental elixir for self-healing. Transpersonal or spiritual self-hypnosis enhances this self-healing process by tapping into a higher, more powerful field of consciousness.

Conclusion

Words have power. It is important to be mindful of the words you say and think. The questions you ask should also not be done lightly; they oftentimes create the resulting thoughts. Self-hypnosis is often amplified when combined with affirmative prayer. The above statements can be verified by applying the principles in this book.

Chapter 15: A Simple Self-Hypnosis Technique

Learning self-hypnosis can be accelerated by seeing a hypnotist and being directly exposed to the hypnotic state. While hypnotized, the hypnotist can teach a trigger that may be used to quickly reenter the hypnotic state. This is typically done by bringing the client in and out of hypnosis a few times, and each time reinforcing the trigger until the client is skilled using the trigger to induce the hypnotic state.

It is not necessary, however, to go to a hypnotist to learn self-hypnosis. With a little practice, the skill can be mastered by anyone. However, we do recommend that you visit a hypnotist recommended by the National Guild of Hypnotists or another legitimate organization to facilitate the process. Like anything else, self-hypnosis improves with practice. Going to a hypnotist first can enhance the process not just by accelerating it, but also because exposure to and learning exactly what a hypnotic state feels like makes it easier to reenter. Partly, this is because like anything else, it is a skill to be learned and will improve the more you do it, but also because the hypnotist can give you a posthypnotic suggestion that will make it easier to reenter the hypnotic state.

The following techniques in hypnosis are designed to be a starting point, not an end point or a destination. They are a basic place to begin a regular practice of self-discovery and personal growth through self-hypnosis. They are not intended to be rigidly followed. The best approach is to use them and adapt or change them as seen fit.

It is recommended that self-hypnosis be practiced at least once a day, twice being the optimum. Mini sessions can be included during the day when a greater skill is achieved entering the hypnotic state. Integration with a practice of periodic self-hypnotic affirmations while awake during the day should also be included. Also, while falling asleep at night and upon waking in the morning silent suggestions and visualizations are an added effect. Our focus now is on the basic self-hypnosis session.

Self-hypnosis is a deceptively easy practice. All that is necessary is to induce a relaxed state and focused attention on the desired outcome. This is done through verbal and visual suggestions. There is an initial induction to relax the body and mind and deepen techniques, then finally there is the verbal and visual imagery designed to direct the body or mind.

Find a quiet place where you won't be interrupted. At first it is better to sit in a comfortable chair rather than lie down. Once you get used to the hypnotic state, then it will be easier to lie down without falling asleep. Also, it is not that important that the chair be extremely comfortable. A standard chair will work as well, but a more comfortable one is preferred. It is important not to cross your legs; this may cut off circulation and cause your legs to fall asleep. Sitting with the spine relatively straight is also desired.

Look toward the top of your head while gently pressing your thumb, index finger, and middle finger together. As your eyes flutter for a few seconds, gently close your eyes. This will serve as a trigger that over time, with repetition, will signal your mind to quickly enter a hypnotic state. If for some reason looking toward the top of your head is too uncomfortable, simply look upward at a point on the wall. Then just allow your eyelids to get heavy and gently close on their own. You can silently suggest that they are getting heavier or even imagine weights on them. Or if either approach seems unnatural for you, simply begin with your eyes closed.

Assuming you are starting with your eyes closed, take a deep breath going in through the nose. Hold it for five seconds, release, and exhale through your mouth. While holding the breath, imagine and say to yourself mentally the letters C–B–A and then exhale. While doing the rhythmic breath, imagine white light entering your body through your nose and exiting through your mouth as you exhale. As you exhale, release your fingers to a natural position. With the exhalation, simply allow or direct your body to relax and breathe normally. When you're skilled with self-hypnosis, this may be all that you need to get into the hypnotic state. In the beginning, however, it will likely require a process of instructing areas of the body to relax. How specifically this is done will depend on how much physical tension is present.

In spiritual or transpersonal hypnosis, divinity is often invoked throughout the process. A simple procedure at this point would be to imagine the white light of divinity or the Holy Spirit to come down through the crown of the head. As it does so, begin to relax the top of your head. As you allow the light to filter down the top of the head, relaxation goes along with it. The scalp relaxes as the light filters down—the eyes, ears, jaw, and chin, neck, and so on.

Once you get to the shoulders, take another deep, rhythmic breath, holding it in for a few seconds, circulating this light, and then exhale to relax the area of the shoulders and the arms and torso. As the light filters down, imagine that every cell, fiber, and subatomic particle of your body is being permeated by and cleansed by the light.

Continue this process all the way down to the feet. Once completed, taking a deep breath, imagining the light going up the feet all the way up to the top of the scalp. Hold it for a few seconds, then exhale while imagining the light going down from the top of the head down the outside of the body to the feet. This can be down a few times to circulate the light energy.

Another technique is to imagine reaching up to the shaft of light coming from the Creator with a brush, and brushing away the areas of tension. This can be done instead, or in combination with, what was just described. The color of the light can also be green or blue, for instance. The point is that it has a relaxing and positive connotation. The light imagery throughout this process should be accompanied by divine infinite love. This is a generic induction. If specific religious imagery is helpful, then incorporate it as seen fit.

This induction process is actually incorporating the healing process into it with the light imagery. As you move on to focus on other aspects of the session, keep in mind that the light is there the whole time, enveloping, protecting, and guiding the session. As you engage in other imagery, the light energy can be called on again.

Once you are past the induction process just described (or some variation of it), it is usually helpful to use a countdown as a deepening technique. A countdown from ten to zero is fine. Silently suggest to yourself that you are going deeper into a relaxed or hypnotic state, occasionally, as you count down with an occasional deep breath as well along the way. You may also imagine walking downstairs or a into tunnel of some sort, but that is not necessary.

When done with the countdown, imagine entering a private safe place that only you may enter. This could be a garden, beach, any place that feels like "home." It could be a totally imaginary place as well. You will want to engage all of your senses and emotions to engage the secret place. Take a few moments to enjoy the feelings of love and relaxation of the hypnotic state here. Safe place or special place imagery is not necessary, but it is very common and may help spur the imagination, especially as it is practiced.

At this point you can give yourself verbal suggestions for whatever you are working on. Always use positive suggestions. You may imagine the healing taking place. It is important to identify with the healed state. There is really no limit to the imagery that may be used. You can imagine a waterfall, flowing through the area that needs to be healed. A cartoon may work well for some. Imagining an injection or real procedure being done may work for other people. Drinking a healing fluid may work well, too. Archetypes may be used as well. Imagining wearing special clothes, granting healing, or increased athletic ability, may work, for instance. For other people imagining cells regenerating may do it. The point is to use an imaginary device that works for you, something that can inspire or spur your imagination. Something you can identify with and believe in and emotionalize makes the morphic field structurally sound.

If there are specific physical symptoms, the process previously described for releasing them would be done in conjunction with the imagery. Or right before or afterward.

After the imagery of the healing device is used, then the focus should be direct toward imagining the healing as if already done. Here gratitude and total emotional engagement should be used. It may help to not only see a still image, but a moving picture of you interacting with the world in a healthy state.

Finally, once this is completed, a simple count up from one to five should be done to leave the self-hypnotic state. Instruct yourself to become more alert and awake with each count. Then open your eyes, and go about your day.

There are countless ways to do a hypnotic induction, as there are for suggestions and visualizations. Develop what works for you. Experiment and vary techniques as needed. Repetition, motivation, and belief are the key.

To recap, there is an induction that will shorten over time. Then there is a deepening technique, usually in the form of a countdown. Following that there is a safe place, then there are the actual suggestive devices, visual and verbal, followed by imagining the healing complete, and then finally, leaving the hypnotic state.

Conclusion

A basic self-hypnosis procedure has been described. As already stated, it is recommended that you visit a hypnotist and be taught self-hypnosis techniques. However, this is not necessary. This basic self-hypnosis session, if applied daily, can have miraculous results.

Pay attention, expect the best, go for it!
Tolly Burkan

Chapter 16: Final Thoughts on Healing

If we look at health as a natural expression of life, then we must also look at healing as an ongoing process of allowing the full expression of life. Typically, we think of healing as a permanent change toward the full expression of health—in other words, full recovery from the illness.

There is nothing wrong with this intention at all. The fact is that virtually every disease or disorder has had people recover from them unexplainably. These people should be sought out. They should be studied and modeled.

However, we must also look at healing as containing levels of gradation. Lessening the symptoms of a disease is a form of healing. Simply managing those symptoms is a form of healing, as is slowing down the progression of the disease and its symptoms, in cases of chronic disease. Even using our mind to make a treatment more effective is a form of healing.

Discernment is required when we are speaking of self-healing or mind-body healing. Restructuring belief systems is required to heal, as is aligning with and identifying with self-empowering healing fields. However, rationalizing guilt over the illness, or being in denial of it, does not serve any purpose. If the body is out of balance, and an illness is expressing itself, then to some degree, it is an acute situation and requires attention.

Discontinuing medications or other treatments abruptly may cause self-harm. If the mind is directed properly, it will make those medications or treatments more effective. Simply saying that an illness is gone will not eliminate the illness unless that belief is dominating at all levels of consciousness. If that belief is dominating at all levels of consciousness then the illness will dissipate on its own.

Reframing and recontextualizing illness is also an important process in healing but also a form of healing as well. There is truth to the aphorism to have an attitude of gratitude. As difficult as this may be, learning to be grateful for the illness is an important process in healing. Finding the lesson to be learned helps one relinquish the illness.

If there was ever a testament to finding purpose or meaning in life, it was recorded by psychiatrist Victor Frankl in *Man's Search for Meaning*. Logotherapy is an approach to therapy guided by finding purpose or meaning in life (Frankl, 1997). The word logotherapy literally means "meaning therapy." Patients are confronted with the meaning of their life and directed toward finding it. Logotherapy asserts that the search for meaning is man's primary purpose. It also asserts that the meaning or purpose to a person's life is unique and specific to them.

This actually coincides well with Hawkins's concept that purpose and meaning and interpretation of reality are derived from a person's predominant level of consciousness. If each individual is aligned with a different field of consciousness, then it would make sense that the purpose and meaning of each individual will be unique. A series of attractors or goals are available within each field.

Unlike psychoanalysis, which was the main psychological theory in the early to mid-twentieth century, logotherapy does not consider man a biological machine who is merely the byproduct of instinctual drives. Instead, man is considered in the context of being a human being who is driven and seeks purpose and meaning. It is an active rather than a reflective therapy. Any analysis that is done, is done with the purpose of eliciting or discovering a person's deepest longings that may be hidden from awareness.

Logotherapy challenges the patient to find that meaning. Tension is used to assist mental health by developing the ability to discover a person's purpose. It argues that a state of being without tension may not benefit a person; instead, it seeks a state of tension that brings forth the striving toward meaning, the creation of a worthwhile goal that is the result of a free choice.

Frankl argues in tangible terms that there is no general meaning to life or general purpose. There is instead a specific purpose of vocation that is unique to each individual. This purpose for existence is unique. Therefore, each individual is unique and irreplaceable.

To understand where Frankl is coming from, it helps to know how he developed logotherapy. Frankl was a victim of German collectivism and socialism in the 1930s. He was to endure the horror and pain of concentration camps during World War II.

It was here that Frankl discovered that the people in the prison camp who lived were the ones who developed a meaning and purpose to live. It didn't matter what that purpose was. For some it was to reunite with their families. For others it was to tell the story of what occurred so it wouldn't happen again.

Frankl had two driving purposes. One was to reunite with his wife. The other was to use his skills as a psychiatrist to write a book about the experience. He played a mental game of sorts by turning the prison camp into a laboratory, a clinical observation of human behavior under the most trying circumstances. It was this meaning and purpose that helped him survive. In his darkest hours it was the goal of publishing his book on his clinical observation of what occurred in the death camp that kept him going.

Frankl describes, without using the word, a hypnotic technique that would get him through the rigors and monotony of forced marches on brutally cold days. With blistered feet and a starving body, Frankl would imagine himself speaking to his class, as if it was already in the past, about the observations he made in the death camp. Repetitive motions and physical activities induced a kind of hypnotic trance. He was able to use this to distract from his pain and keep his future goal at the forefront.

The technique may have been hypnotic, but it was consciously chosen. With the exception of his sister, Frankl's whole family, including his wife, died in those camps or in gas chambers. This is what makes his findings remarkable. Frankl shows that there is a gap between stimulus and response where man has the freedom to choose. Even when the circumstances can't be changed, the attitude about the experience can, in fact, be chosen.

Frankl describes how some of the intellectual and less physically hardy prisoners survived; during their suffering, they went inward and experienced spiritual riches. In his case, he recounts that one frozen night while marching and being beaten occasionally along the way, he thought of his wife, knowing the man marching next to him was doing the same.

As the dawn approached, he recounts that his wife's image was more real than the coming sunrise. He could hear her words and see her expression. Her smile and encouragement imbued him with a will to live. It was then that he realized that it was love itself that was man's highest purpose. Salvation is through love. He experienced bliss in the midst of hell on earth. He understood that suffering in an honorable way can result in loving contemplation and fulfillment.

This inward trek would grow, and transcendent experiences would occur as he observed the beauty of nature during marches. As the external reality grew more grueling, the internal reality of transcending it grew more intense as well. Routinely, Frankl would commune with his wife mentally or spiritually. The divinity of a bowl of soup or some other minor pleasure would be magnified, occasionally giving a brief moment of bliss.

In the camp, those who did not find a future goal to pull them forward fell into retrospective thinking, and eventually apathy and death. To them, the futility and pointlessness of everything became overwhelming. As they focused on the past to distract from the present pain, all meaning was lost. Frankl points out that the enormous pain of the external reality could also become an instrument for enormous spiritual growth. The challenge presented was to either create an internal triumph or to fall into a vegetative state. To survive, faith in the future was required. Without it, men were doomed.

This brings us to Frankl's concept of tragic optimism. In a sense, it is the classic case of turning lemons to lemonade. Tragic optimism basically consists of reframing pain and suffering into triumph and achievement, turning guilt into a prompt for internal change, and using the ever-changing volatile nature of life as an incentive for positive action.

Applying these concepts toward illness changes one from a victim to a victor. Reframing and recontextualizing is the key. It is recommended that a dual goal be held in mind. Healing in the physical or mental sense—or both, depending on the illness—and spiritual growth must be pursued. If healing on all levels is the goal, then a continuum of healing would entail physical, psychological, and spiritual healing.

This approach gives purpose and meaning to illness—not as a thing in itself to be clung to but as a prompt for spiritual growth. Socrates taught that the enlightenment of the soul was the purpose of human existence (Hawkins D. R., 2002). For some of us, an illness or a disease is the gadfly constantly reminding us and prompting us toward that purpose.

The ability to be grateful opens up the doorway to acceptance and the ensuing spiritual growth that occurs. Recognizing that the illness may be there to prompt spiritual growth, and the willingness to grow spiritually, is the ultimate form of healing. Physical healing may or may not happen. The expanding of awareness and the opening of higher levels of reality may, in fact, be the result of a necessary illness.

Being a martyr due to physical or even mental illness is not what is being promoted here. It is the exact opposite. The identification is not with the illness; the spiritual reality that is you is being advocated. There can be no better expression of life than spiritual growth. All spiritual growth brings a person closer to the Creator in some way or form. Spiritual growth is a process of relinquishing the inherent limitations of perception.

Ultimately, physical death is inevitable. In this course of life, even the flunkies eventually graduate. Death itself is a process of relinquishing the limitations of perception inherent in a localized existence. It is a blending with eternal consciousness. The illusion of nonexistence is finally discarded. Eternity becomes reality.

About the Author

Joseph Sansone is a consulting hypnotist. He was trained in advanced clinical hypnosis at the Academy of Professional Hypnosis

The techniques in this book have been used successfully by this author to heal an injured neck and to restore vision in the left eye after being blind for three days due to a hemorrhage in the retina. Diagnosed with type 1 diabetes in childhood, healing and self-restoration are an ongoing process for this writer.

References

(n.d.). Retrieved from APA.org: http://www.apa.org/topics/hypnosis/media.aspx

(n.d.). Retrieved from CDC.gov: http://www.cdc.gov/reproductivehealth/MaternalInfantHealth/PretermBirth.htm

(n.d.). Retrieved from ATA.org: http://www.ata.org/for-patients/faqs

(n.d.). Retrieved from Psoriasis.org: https://www.psoriasis.org/about-psoriasis

(n.d.). Retrieved from Stroke.org: http://www.stroke.org/site/DocServer/STROKE_101_Fact_Sheet.pdf?docID=4541

(n.d.). Retrieved from WebMD.com: http://www.webmd.com/allergies/guide/allergy-basics

(n.d.). Retrieved from NIH.gov: http://www.nhlbi.nih.gov/health/health-topics/topics/asthma/

(n.d.). Retrieved from NIH.gov: http://www.nhlbi.nih.gov/health/health-topics/topics/angioplasty/

(n.d.). Retrieved from NationalMSSociety.org: http://www.nationalmssociety.org/about-multiple-sclerosis/what-we-know-about-ms/what-is-ms/index.aspx

(n.d.). Retrieved from MayoClinic.com : http://www.mayoclinic.com/health/parkinsons-disease/DS00295

(n.d.). Retrieved from NIH.gov: http://www.nhlbi.nih.gov/health/health-topics/topics/hemophilia/

(n.d.). Retrieved from CDC.gov: http://www.cdc.gov/arthritis/basics/fibromyalgia.htm

(n.d.). Retrieved from NIH.gov: http://www.nhlbi.nih.gov/health/health-topics/topics/sca/

(n.d.). Retrieved from NIH.gov: http://www.nlm.nih.gov/medlineplus/raynaudsdisease.html

(n.d.). Retrieved from Faustmanlab.org: www.faustmanlab.org

(n.d.). Retrieved from MayoClinic.com: http://www.mayoclinic.com/health/rheumatoid-arthritis/DS00020

(n.d.). Retrieved from WND.com: http://www.wnd.com/2003/02/17494/

(n.d.). Retrieved from EdgarCayce.org: http://www.edgarcayce.org/are/edgarcayce.aspx

(n.d.). Retrieved from EdgarCayce.org: http://www.edgarcayce.org/are/edgarcayce.aspx?id=2497

(n.d.). Retrieved from Law.onecle.com: http://law.onecle.com/florida/regulation-of-professions-and-occupations/chapter485.html

(n.d.). Retrieved from NGH.net: http://ngh.net/wp-content/uploads/2010/11/StateLawGuide.pdf

(n.d.). Retrieved from NationalHealthFreedom.org: http://www.nationalhealthfreedom.org/state_organizations.html

Abrahamsen, R., Baad-Hansen, L., & Svensson, P. (2008). Hypnosis in the management of persistent idiopathic orofacial pain–clinical and psychosocial findings. Pain. *Pain, 136*(1), 44-52.

Abramowitz, E. G., & Lichtenberg, P. (2009). Hypnotherapeutic olfactory conditioning (hoc): Case studies of needle phobia, panic disorder, and combat-induced PTSD. *Intl. Journal of Clinical and Experimental Hypnosis, 57*(2), 184–197.

Abramowitz, E. G., Barak, Y., Ben-Avi, I., & Knobler, H. Y. (2008). Hypnotherapy in the treatment of chronic combat-related PTSD patients suffering from insomnia: A randomized, zolpidem-controlled clinical trial. *Intl. Journal of Clinical and Experimental Hypnosis, 56*(3), 270–280.

Ahmad, B., & Zaman, K. (2011). Alternatives to simply forgiving and forgetting: Comparing techniques in hypnosis, NLP and time line therapy™ in reducing the intensity of memories of stressful events. Stress and Health. *Stress and Health, 27*(3), 241–250.

Alladin, A., & Alibhai, A. (2007). Cognitive hypnotherapy for depression: An empirical investigation. *Intl. Journal of Clinical and Experimental Hypnosis, 55*(2), 147–166.

Anbar, R. D., & Slothower, M. P. (2006). Hypnosis for treatment of insomnia in school-age children: a retrospective chart review. *BMC pediatrics, 6*(1), 23.

Aronoff, G. M., Aronoff, S., & Peck, L. W. (1975). Hypnotherapy in the treatment of bronchial asthma. *Annals of allergy, 34*(6), 356.

Asch, S. E. (1956). Studies of independence and conformity: I. A minority of one against a unanimous majority. *Psychological Monographs: General and Applied, 70*(9), 1–70.

asch.net. (n.d.). Retrieved from http://www.asch.net/Home/tabid/37/Default.aspx

Attias, J., Shemesh, Z., Sohmer, H., Gold, S., Shoham, C., & Faraggi, D. (1993). Comparison between self-hypnosis, masking and attentiveness for alleviation of chronic tinnitus. *International Journal of Audiology, 32*(3), 205–212.

Bakke, A. C., Purtzer, M. Z., & Newton, P. (2002). The effect of hypnotic-guided imagery on psychological well-being and immune function in patients with prior breast cancer. *Journal of psychosomatic research, 53*(6), 1131–1137.

Barber, T. X. (1978). Hypnosis, suggestions, and psychosomatic phenomena: A new look from the standpoint of recent experimental studies. *American Journal of Clinical Hypnosis, 1*, 13–27.

Barrios, M. V., & Singer, J. L. (1981). The treatment of creative blocks: A comparison of waking imagery, hypnotic dream, and rational discussion techniques. *Imagination, Cognition and Personality, 1*(1), 89–109.

Ben-Zvi, Z., Spohn, W. A., Young, S. H., & Kattan, M. (1982). Hypnosis for exercise-induced asthma. *The American review of respiratory disease, 125*(4), 392.

Berger, M. M., Davadant, M., Marin, C., Wasserfallen, J. B., Pinget, C., Maravic, P., & Chiolero, R. L. (2010). Impact of a pain protocol including hypnosis in major burns. *Burns, 36*(5), 639–646.

Berman, B. M., Lao, L., Langenberg, P., Lee, W. L., Gilpin, A. M., & Hochberg, M. C. (2004). Effectiveness of Acupuncture as Adjunctive Therapy in Osteoarthritis of the KneeA Randomized, Controlled Trial. Annals of internal medicine. *Annals of internal medicine, 141*(12), 901–910.

Bohm, D. (2008). *Wholeness and the implicate order.* New York: Routledge.

Braid, J. (1843). *Neurypnology; or, the rationale of nervous sleep, considered in relation with animal magnetism.*

Braid, J. (1843). Neurypnology; or, the rationale of nervous sleep, considered in relation with animal magnetism.

Bruce, S., Allen, C., & John, B. (1996). *Textbook Of Transpersonal Psychiatry And Psychology.* New York: Basic Books.

Bryant, R. A., Moulds, M. L., Guthrie, R. M., & Nixon, R. D. (2005). The additive benefit of hypnosis and cognitive-behavioral therapy in treating acute stress disorder. *Journal of Consulting and Clinical Psychology, 73*(2), 334.

Burkan, T. (2001). *Extreme Spirituality: Radical Journeys for the Inward Bound.* Beyond Words Pub Co; First edition. edition (October 10, 2001).

Calvert, E. L., Houghton, L. A., Cooper, P., Morris, J., & Whorwell, P. J. (2002). Long-term improvement in functional dyspepsia using hypnotherapy., 123(6), 1778-1785. *Gastroenterology, 6*, 1778–1785.

Cancer.gov. (n.d.). Retrieved from http://www.cancer.gov/cancertopics/cancerlibrary/what-is-cancer

Capra, F. (2010). *The Tao of Physics.* Boston: Shambhala Publications Inc.

Cardeña, E., Svensson, C., & Hejdström, F. (2013). Hypnotic Tape Intervention Ameliorates Stress: A Randomized, Control Study. *International Journal of Clinical and Experimental Hypnosis, 61*(2), 125–145.

Carmody, T. P., Duncan, C., Simon, J. A., Solkowitz, S., Huggins, J., Lee, S., & Delucchi, K. (2008). Hypnosis for smoking cessation: a randomized trial. *Nicotine & tobacco research, 10*(5), 811–818.

Carnahan, L. F., Ritterband, L. M., Bailey, E., Thorndike, F. P., Lord, H. R., & Baum, L. D. (2010). Results from a study examining the feasibility and preliminary efficacy of a self-hypnosis intervention available on the Web for cancer survivors with insomnia. *E-Journal of Applied Psychology, 6*(2), 10–23.

Carter, C. (2012). *Science And The Afterlife Experience.* Rochester: Inner Tradiutions.

Castel, A., Pérez, M., Sala, J., Padrol, A., & Rull, M. (2007). Effect of hypnotic suggestion on fibromyalgic pain: comparison between hypnosis and relaxation. *European Journal of Pain, 11*(4), 463–468.

Castel, A., Salvat, M., Sala, J., & Rull, M. (n.d.). Castel, A., Salvat, M., Sala, J., & Rull, M. (2009). Cognitive-behavioural group treatment with hypnosis: a randomized pilot trail in fibromyalgia. *Contemporary hypnosis, 26*(1), 48–59.

Catoire, P., Delaunay, L., Dannappel, T., Baracchini, D., Marcadet-Fredet, S., Moreau, O., & Marret, E. (2013). Hypnosis versus Diazepam for Embryo Transfer: A Randomized Controlled Study. *American Journal of Clinical Hypnosis, 55*(4), 378–386.

Caton, R. (1898). TWO LECTURES on the TEMPLES and RITUAL of ASKLEPIOS at EPIDAURUS and ATHENS: Delivered at the Royal Institution of Great Britain. *British medical journal, 1*(1955), 1572.

Cleland, J. (1953). The healing Art in Primitive Society. The Australian Journal of Anthropology. *The Australian Journal of Anthropology*, 395–411.

Collison, D. R. (1975). Which asthmatic patients should be treated by hypnotherapy?. *The Medical journal of Australia*, 776–781.

Conn, L., & Mott Jr, T. (1984). Plethysmographic demonstration of rapid vasodilation by direct suggestion: A case of Raynaud's Disease treated by hypnosis. American Journal of Clinical Hypnosis. *American Journal of Clinical Hypnosis, 26*(3), 166–170.

Cordi, M. J., Schlarb, A. A., & Rasch, B. (2014). Deepening sleep by hypnotic suggestion. Sleep, *37*(6), 1143.

Corey Brown, D., & Corydon Hammond, D. (2007). Evidence-based clinical hypnosis for obstetrics, labor and delivery, and preterm labor. *Intl. Journal of Clinical and Experimental Hypnosis, 55*(3), 355–371.

Coué, E. (1922). *Self mastery through conscious autosuggestion.* Malkan Publishing Company.

Craciun, B., Holdevici, I., & Craciun, A. (2012). The efficiency of ericksonian hypnosis in diminishing stress and procrastination in patients with generalized anxiety disorder. *European Psychiatry, 27*(1), 1136.

Cromie, W. J. (2002, April 18). Meditation changes temperatures. *Harvard Gazette.*

Cupal, D. D., & Brewer, B. W. (2001). Effects of relaxation and guided imagery on knee strength, reinjury anxiety, and pain following anterior cruciate ligament reconstruction. *Rehabilitation Psychology, 46*(1), 28.

Cyna, A. M., Andrew, M. I., & McAuliffe, G. L. (2006). Antenatal self-hypnosis for labour and childbirth: a pilot study. *Anaesthesia and Intensive Care, 34*(4), 464–469.

Dane, J. R. (1996). Hypnosis for pain and neuromuscular rehabilitation with multiple sclerosis: Case summary, literature review, and analysis of outcomes. *International Journal of Clinical and Experimental Hypnosis,* 44(3), 208–231.

Danucalov, M. A., Simoes, R. S., Kozasa, E. H., & Leite, J. R. (2008). Cardiorespiratory and metabolic changes during yoga sessions: the effects of respiratory exercises and meditation practices. *Applied psychophysiology and biofeedback, 39*(2), 77–81.

Davison, G. C., & Singleton, L. (1967). A preliminary report of improved vision under hypnosis. *The International journal of clinical and experimental hypnosis, 15*(2), 57–62.

Deabler, H. L., Fidel, E., Dillenkoffer, R. L., & Elder, S. T. (1973). The use of relaxation and hypnosis in lowering high blood pressure. *American Journal of Clinical Hypnosis, 16*(2), 75–83.

Decety, J. (1996). Do imagined and executed actions share the same neural substrate? *Cognitive brain research, 3*(2), 87–93.

Derbyshire, S. W., Whalley, M. G., & Oakley, D. A. (2009). Fibromyalgia pain and its modulation by hypnotic and nonhypnotic suggestion: An fMRI analysis. *European Journal of Pain, 13*(5), 542–550.

Derbyshire, S. W., Whalley, M. G., Stenger, V. A., & Oakley, D. A. (2004). Cerebral activation during hypnotically induced and imagined pain. *NeuroImage, 23*(1), 392–401.

Diamond, S. G., Davis, O. C., Schaechter, J. D., & Howe, R. D. (2006). Hypnosis for rehabilitation after stroke: six case studies. *Contemporary Hypnosis, 23*(4), 173–180.

Diego, M. A., Field, T., Hernandez-Reif, M., Cullen, C., Schanberg, S., & Kuhn, C. (2004). Prepartum, postpartum, and chronic depression effects on newborns. *Psychiatry: Interpersonal and Biological Processes, 67*(1), 63–80.

Dinges, D. F., Whitehouse, W. G., Orne, E. C., Bloom, P. B., Carlin, M. M., Bauer, N. K., & Orne, M. T. (1997). Self-hypnosis training as an adjunctive treatment in the management of pain associated with sickle cell disease. *International Journal of Clinical and Experimental Hypnosis, 45*(4), 417–432.

Doidge, N. (2007). *The Brain That Changes Itself.* New York: The Penguin Group.

Donaldson, V. W. (2000). A clinical study of visualization on depressed white blood cell count in medical patients. 25(2). *Applied psychophysiology and biofeedback, 25*(2), 117–128.

Dubin, L. L., & Shapiro, S. S. (1974). Use of hypnosis to facilitate dental extraction and hemostasis in a classic hemophiliac with a high antibody titer to factor VIII. *American Journal of Clinical Hypnosis, 17*(2), 79–83.

Dubrov, A. P., & Pushkin, V. N. (1982). *Parapsychology and contemporary science. Consultants Bureau.* New York: Consultants Bureau.

Eitner, S. W. (2006). Rapid induction of hypnosis by finger elongation: A brief communication. *Intl. Journal of Clinical and Experimental Hypnosis, 54*(3), 245–262.

Eitner, S., Wichmann, M., & Holst, S. (2005). "Hypnopuncture"—A dental-emergency treatment concept for patients with a distinctive gag reflex. *International Journal of Clinical and Experimental Hypnosis, 53*(1), 60–73.

Eitner, S., Wichmann, M., & Holst, S. (2005). A long-term therapeutic treatment for patients with a severe gag reflex. *Intl. Journal of Clinical and Experimental Hypnosis, 53*(1), 74–86.

Elahi, Z., Boostani, R., & Motie Nasrabadi, A. (2012). Estimation of hypnosis susceptibility based on electroencephalogram signal features. *Scientia Iranica, 20*(3), 730–737.

Elkins, G. J. (2013). A Pilot Investigation of Guided Self-Hypnosis in the Treatment of Hot Flashes Among Postmenopausal Women. *International Journal of Clinical and Experimental Hypnosis, 61*(3), 342–350.

Elkins, G. R., & Rajab, M. H. (2004). Clinical hypnosis for smoking cessation: Preliminary results of a three-session intervention. *International Journal of Clinical and Experimental Hypnosis, 52*(1), 73-91.

Elkins, G., Jensen, M. P., & Patterson, D. R. (2007). Hypnotherapy for the management of chronic pain. *Intl. Journal of Clinical and Experimental Hypnosis, 55*(3), 275–287.

Elkins, G., Marcus, J., Bates, J., Hasan Rajab, M., & Cook, T. (2006). Intensive hypnotherapy for smoking cessation: A prospective study 1. *Intl. Journal of Clinical and Experimental Hypnosis, 54*(3), 303–315.

Elkins, G., Sliwinski, J., Bowers, J., & Encarnacion, E. (2013). Feasibility of Clinical Hypnosis For The Treatment of Parkinson's Disease: A Case Study. *International Journal of Clinical and Experimental Hypnosis, 61*(2), 172–182.

Eremin, O., Walker, M. B., Simpson, E., Heys, S. D., Ah-See, A. K., Hutcheon, A. W., & Walker, L. G. (2009). Immuno-modulatory effects of relaxation training and guided imagery in women with locally advanced breast cancer undergoing multimodality therapy: A randomised controlled trial. *The Breast, 18*(1), 17–25.

Erickson, M. H. (1964). The confusion technique in hypnosis. *American Journal of Clinical Hypnosis, 6*(3), 183–207.

Esdaile, J. (1846). *Mesmerism in India: And its practical application in surgery and medicine.* Longman, Brown, Green, and Longmans.

Esdaile, J. (1846). *Mesmerism in India: And its practical application in surgery and medicine.* Longman, Brown, Green, and Longmans.

Facco, E., Pasquali, S., Zanette, G., & Casiglia, E. (2013). Hypnosis as sole anaesthesia for skin tumour removal in a patient with multiple chemical sensitivity. *Anaesthesia.*

Faymonville, M. E., Mambourg, P. H., Joris, J., Vrijens, B., Fissette, J., Albert, A., & Lamy, M. (1997). Psychological approaches during conscious sedation. Hypnosis versus stress reducing strategies: a prospective randomized study. *Pain, 73*(3), 361–367.

Fenwick, P., & Fenwick, E. (2012). *The Truth in the Light.* White Crow Books.

Festinger, L. (1962). *A theory of cognitive dissonance (Vol. 2). Stanford university press.* (Vol. 2). Palo Alto, California: Stanford university press.

Fillmer, H. T. (1980). Improving Reading Performances through Hypnosis. *Community College Review, 2,* 58–62.

Frankl, V. E. (1997). *Man's Search For Menaing.* New York: Pocket Books; Rev Upd edition.

Freeman, R., Barabasz, A., Barabasz, M., & Warner, D. (2000). Hypnosis and distraction differ in their effects on cold pressor pains. *American Journal of Clinical Hypnosis, 43*(2), 137–148.

Fry, L., Mason, A. A., & Pearson, R. B. (1964). Effect of hypnosis on allergic skin responses in asthma and hay-fever. *British Medical Journal,* 1145.

Gajan, F., Pannetier, B., Cordier, A., Amstutz-Montadert, I., Dehesdin, D., & Marie, J. P. (2011). Role of hypnotherapy in the treatment of debilitating tinnitus. *Revue de laryngologie-otologie-rhinologie, 133*(3), 147.

Ganis, G., Thompson, W. L., & Kosslyn, S. M. (2004). Brain areas underlying visual mental imagery and visual perception: an fMRI study. *Cognitive Brain Research, 20*(2), 226–241.

Giles, C. S. (2003). *NGH.NET*. Retrieved from National Guild Of Hypnot6ists: http://ngh.net/wp-content/uploads/2010/12/GilesCancerStudy.pdf

Ginandes, C. S., & Rosenthal, D. I. (1999). Using hypnosis to accelerate the healing of bone fractures: a randomized controlled pilot study. *Alternative Therapies in Health and Medicine, 5*(2), 67.

Ginandes, C., Brooks, P., Sando, W., Jones, C., & Aker, J. (2003). Can medical hypnosis accelerate post-surgical wound healing? Results of a clinical trial. *American Journal of Clinical Hypnosis, 45*(4), 333–351.

Goldfine, I. D., Abraira, C., Gruenewald, D., & Goldstein, M. S. (1970). Plasma insulin levels during imaginary food ingestion under hypnosis. *Proceedings of the Society for Experimental Biology and Medicine. Society for Experimental Biology and Medicine, 133*(1), 274–276.

Gonsalkorale, W. M., & Whorwell, P. J. (2005). Hypnotherapy in the treatment of irritable bowel syndrome. *European Journal of Gastroenterology & Hepatology, 17*(1), 15–20.

Grabowska, M. J. (1971). The effect of hypnosis and hypnotic suggestion on the blood flow in the extremities. *Polish Medical Journal*.

Graham, C., & Leibowitz, H. W. (1972). The effect of suggestion on visual acuity, *International Journal of Clinical and Experimental Hypnosis, 20*(3), 169–186.

Grøntved, A., & Hu, F. B. (2011). Television viewing and risk of type 2 diabetes, cardiovascular disease, and all-cause mortality. *JAMA, 305*(23), 2448.

Gur, R. C., & Reyher, J. (1976). Enhancement of creativity via free-imagery and hypnosis. *American Journal of Clinical Hypnosis, 18*(4), 237–249.

Guttman, K., & Ball, T. S. (2013). An unanticipated allergic reaction to a hypnotic suggestion for anesthesia: a brief communication and commentary. *International Journal of Clinical and Experimental Hypnosis, 61*(3), 336–341.

Halsband, U., Mueller, S., Hinterberger, T., & Strickner, S. (2009). Plasticity changes in the brain in hypnosis and meditation. *Contemporary Hypnosis, 26*(4), 194–215.

Hammer, E. F. (1954). Post-hypnotic suggestion and test performance. *International Journal of Clinical and Experimental Hypnosis, 2*(3), 178–185.

Hammond, D. C. (2007). Review of the efficacy of clinical hypnosis with headaches and migraines. *Intl. Journal of Clinical and Experimental Hypnosis, 55*(2), 207–219.

Hammond, D. C. (2010). Hypnosis in the treatment of anxiety and stress related disorders. *Expert Review of Neurotherapeutic, 10*(2), 263–273.

Han, J. S. (2004). Acupuncture and endorphins. *Neuroscience letters, 361*(1), 258–261.

Harmon, T. M., Hynan, M. T., & Tyre, T. E. (1990). Improved obstetric outcomes using hypnotic analgesia and skill mastery combined with childbirth education. *Journal of Consulting and Clinical Psychology, 58*(5), 525.

Hawkins, D. R. (2002). *Power.* Carlsbad, CA: Hay House; 1st edition.

Hawkins, D. R. (2002). *Power vs. Force.* Carlsbad, CA: Hay House.

Hawkins, D. R. (2009). *Healing and Recovery.* Sedona: Veritas Publishing.

Hawkins, D. R. (2012). *Letting Go: The Pathway of Surrender.* Sedona: Veritas Publising.

Hawkins, P., & Polemikos, N. (2002). Hypnosis treatment of sleeping problems in children experiencing loss. *Contemporary Hypnosis, 19*(1), 18–24.

Hill, N. (1987). *Think and Grow Rich.* New York: The Ballantine Publishing Group; 1st edition.

Hoeft, F., Gabrieli, J. D., Whitfield-Gabrieli, S., Haas, B. W., Bammer, R., Menon, V., & Spiegel, D. (2012). Functional brain basis of hypnotizabilityfunctional brain basis of hypnotizability. *Archives of General Psychiatry, 69*(10), 1064–1072.

Horton-hausknecht, J. R., Mitzdorf, U., & Melchart, D. (2000). The effect of hypnosis therapy on the symptoms and disease activity in rheumatoid arthritis. *Psychology & Health, 14*(6), 1089–1104.

Hui, K. K., Liu, J., Makris, N., Gollub, R. L., Chen, A. J., I Moore, C., & Kwong, K. K. (2000). Acupuncture modulates the limbic system and subcortical gray structures of the human brain: evidence from fMRI studies in normal subjects. *Human Brain Mapping, 9*(1), 13–25.

Hunt, V. V. (1996). *Infinite Mind.* Malibu: Malibu Publishing Co.

Hunt, V. V. (1996). *Infinite Mind: Human Vibrations of Consciousness.* Malibu: Malibu Publishing Co.

Hunt, V. V. (1996). *Infinite Mind: Science of the Vibrations of Consciousness.* Malibu, CA: Malibu Publishing Co.

Illovsky, J. (1963). An experience with group hypnosis in reading disability in primary behavior disorders. *The Journal of Genetic Psychology, 102*(1), 61-67.

Jacobson, N. K. (2011). The effects of encoding in hypnosis and post-hypnotic suggestion on academic performance. *American Journal of Clinical Hypnosis, 53*(4), 247-254.

James, W. (2009). *The Varieties Of Religious Experience: A Study In Human Nature.* Seven Treasures Publications.

Jensen, M. P., Barber, J., Romano, J. M., Molton, I. R., Raichle, K. A., Osborne, T. L., & Patterson, D. R. (2009). A comparison of self-hypnosis versus progressive muscle relaxation in patients with multiple sclerosis and chronic pain. *Intl. Journal of Clinical and Experimental Hypnosis, 57*(2), 198–221.

Jensen, M. P., McArthur, K. D., Barber, J., Hanley, M. A., Engel, J. M., Romano, J. M., & Patterson, D. R. (2006). Satisfaction with, and the beneficial side effects of, hypnotic analgesia. *International Journal of Clinical and Experimental Hypnosis, 54*(4), 432–447.

Johnston, M. F., Ortiz Sánchez, E., Vujanovic, N. L., & Li, W. (2011). Acupuncture may stimulate anticancer immunity via activation of natural killer cells. *Evidence-Based Complementary and Alternative Medicine.*

Jung, C. G. (1936). The concept of the collective unconscious. *Collected works, 9*(1), 42.

Kaminsky, D., Rosca, P., Budowski, D., Korin, Y., & Yakhnich, L. (2008). Group hypnosis treatment of drug addicts. *Harefuah, 147*(8-9), 679.

Kirsch, I., & Low, C. B. (2013). Suggestion in the treatment of depression. *American Journal of Clinical Hypnosis, 55*(3), 221–229.

Kirsch, I., Montgomery, G., & Sapirstein, G. (1995). Hypnosis as an adjunct to cognitive-behavioral psychotherapy: a meta-analysis. 214. *Journal of consulting and clinical psychology, 2,* 214.

Koe, G. G., & Oldridge, O. A. (1988). The effect of hypnotically induced suggestions on reading performance. *International Journal of Clinical and Experimental Hypnosis, 36*(4), 275–283.

Kohen, D. P., & Zajac, R. (2007). Self-hypnosis training for headaches in children and adolescents. *The Journal of Pediatrics, 150*(6), 635–639.

Kraft, D. (2012). Panic disorder without agoraphobia. A multimodal approach: solution-focused therapy, hypnosis and psychodynamic psychotherapy. *Journal of Integrative Research, Counselling and Psychotherapy, 1*(1), 4–15.

Kraft, T. &. (2004). Creating a virtual reality in hypnosis: A case of driving phobia. Contemporary Hypnosis. *21*(2), 79–85.

Kubler-Ross, E. (2008). *On Life after Death, revised.* Berkeley: Celestial Arts; 2nd edition.

LA Times. (n.d.). Retrieved from http://articles.latimes.com/1987-02-02/local/me-134_1_hypnotist.

Lamsa, G. M. (1985). *Holy Bible From The Ancient Eastern Text: George M. Lamsa's translation From The Aramaic Of The Peshitta.* New York: Harper & Row; Revised edition.

Lang, E. V., Benotsch, E. G., Fick, L. J., Lutgendorf, S., Berbaum, M. L., Berbaum, K. S., & Spiegel, D. (2000). Adjunctive nonpharmacological analgesia for invasive medical procedures: a randomised trial. *The Lancet, 355*(9214), 1486–1490.

Langer, E., Djikic, M., Pirson, M., Madenci, A., & Donohue, R. (2010). Believing is seeing using mindlessness (mindfully) to improve visual acuity. *Psychological Science, 21*(5), 661–666.

Lee, J. S., & Koo, B. H. (2012). Fractal analysis of EEG upon auditory stimulation during waking and hypnosis in healthy volunteers. *International Journal of Clinical and Experimental Hypnosis, 60*(3), 266–285.

Leuchter, A. F., Cook, I. A., Witte, E. A., Morgan, M., & Abrams, M. (2002). Changes in brain function of depressed subjects during treatment with placebo. *American Journal of Psychiatry, 159*(1), 122–129.

Levitas, E., Parmet, A., Lunenfeld, E., Bentov, Y., Burstein, E., Friger, M., & Potashnik, G. (2006). Impact of hypnosis during embryo transfer on the outcome of in vitro fertilization—embryo transfer: a case-control study. *Fertility and Sterility, 85*(5), 1404–1408.

Liossi, C., & Hatira, P. (2003). Clinical hypnosis in the alleviation of procedure-related pain in pediatric oncology patients. *International Journal of Clinical and Experimental Hypnosis, 51*(1), 4–28.

Liossi, C., & P., H. (1999). Clinical hypnosis versus cognitive behavioral training for pain management for pediatric cancer patients undergoing bone marrow aspirations. *International Journal of Clinical and Experimental Hypnosis, 47*(2), 104–116.

Liossi, C., & White, P. (2001). Efficacy of clinical hypnosis in the enhancement of quality of life of terminally ill cancer patients. *Contemporary Hypnosis. 18*(3), 145–160.

Liossi, C., White, P., & Hatira, P. (2006). Randomized clinical trial of local anesthetic versus a combination of local anesthetic with self-hypnosis in the management of pediatric procedure-related pain. *Health Psychology, 25*(3), 307.

Lipton, B. (2008). *The Biology of belief.* Carlsbad, CA: Hay House.

Lorenz, E. (1995). *The Essence Of Chaos: (Jessie and John Danz Lecture Series).* Seattle: University of Washington Press.

Lu, D. P. (2001). Acupuncture and clinical hypnosis for facial and head and neck pain: a single crossover comparison. *American Journal of Clinical Hypnosis, 44*(2), 141–148.

Machovec, F. J. (1975). Hypnosis before Mesmer. *American Journal of Clinical Hypnosis, 17*(4), 215–220.

Machovec, F. J. (1979). The cult of Asklipios. American Journal of Clinical Hypnosis. *22*(20), 85–90.

Madrid, A., Rostel, G., Pennington, D., & Murphy, D. (1995). Subjective assessment of allergy relief following group hypnosis and self-hypnosis: a preliminary study. *American Journal of Clinical Hypnosis, 38*(2), 80–86.

Maher-Loughnan, G. P. (1970). Hypnosis and autohypnosis for the treatment of asthma. *International Journal of Clinical and Experimental Hypnosis, 18*(1), 1–14.

Maher-Loughnan, G. P., Macdonald, N., Mason, A. A., & Fry, L. (1962). Controlled trial of hypnosis in the symptomatic treatment of asthma. *British Medical Journal,* 371.

Manganiello, A. J. (1984). A comparative study of hypnotherapy and psychotherapy in the treatment of methadone addicts. *American Journal of Clinical Hypnosis, 26*(4), 273–279.

Manganiello, A. J. (1986). Hypnotherapy in the rehabilitation of a stroke victim: a case study. *American Journal of Clinical Hypnosis, 29*(1), 64-68.

Martens, J. W., Koehler, P. J., & Vijselaar, J. (2013). Magnetic flimmers: light in the electromagnetic darkness. *Brain, 136*(3), 971–979.

Mason, A. A. (1952). Case of congenital ichthyosiform erythrodermia of Brocq treated by hypnosis. *British Medical Journal,* 422.

McClenon, J. (1997). Shamanic healing, human evolution, and the origin of religion. *Journal for the Scientific Study of Religion,* 345–354.

McConnell, M. J., Lindberg, M. R., Brennand, K. J., Piper, J. C., Voet, T., Cowing-Zitron, C., & Gage, F. H. (2013). Mosaic copy number variation in human neurons. *Science, 342*(6158), 632–637.

McGeown, W. J., Mazzoni, G., Venneri, A., & Kirsch, I. (2009). Hypnotic induction decreases anterior default mode activity. *Consciousness and Cognition, 18*(4), 848–855.

McTaggart, L. (2008). *The Field: The Quest For The Secret Force OF The Universe.* New York: Harper Collins.

Medterms.com. (n.d.). Retrieved from http://www.medterms.com/script/main/art.asp?articlekey=40362

Mehl-Madrona, L. E. (2004). Hypnosis to facilitate uncomplicated birth. *American Journal of Clinical Hypnosis, 46*(4), 299–312.

Milgram, S. (1963). Behavioral study of obedience. *The Journal of Abnormal and Social Psychology, 67*(4), 371.

Miller, S. D. (1989). Optical differences in cases of multiple personality disorder. *The Journal of nervous and mental disease, 177*(8), 480–486.

Miller, V., & Whorwell, P. J. (2008). Treatment of inflammatory bowel disease: A role for hypnotherapy? 56(3). *Intl. Journal of Clinical and Experimental Hypnosis, 56*(3), 306–317.

Mirzamani, S. M., Bahrami, H., Moghtaderi, S., & Namegh, M. (2012). The effectiveness of hypnotherapy in treating depression, anxiety and sleep disturbance caused by subjective tinnitus. *Zahedan Journal of Research in Medical Sciences, 14*(9), 76–79.

Monroe, R. A. (1992). *Far Journeys.* New York: Broadway Books.

Montgomery, G. H., David, D., Kangas, M., Green, S., Sucala, M., Bovbjerg, D. H., & Schnur, J. B. (2014). Randomized controlled trial of a cognitive-behavioral therapy plus hypnosis intervention to control fatigue in patients undergoing radiotherapy for breast cancer. *Journal of Clinical Oncology.*

Montgomery, G. H., David, D., Winkel, G., Silverstein, J. H., & Bovbjerg, D. H. (2002). The effectiveness of adjunctive hypnosis with surgical patients: a meta-analysis. *Anesthesia & Analgesia, 94*(6), 1639–1645.

Montgomery, G. H., DuHamel, K. N., & Redd, W. H. (2000). A meta-analysis of hypnotically induced analgesia: how effective is hypnosis? *International Journal of Clinical and Experimental Hypnosis, 48*(2), 138–153.

Montgomery, G. H., Weltz, C. R., Seltz, M., & Bovbjerg, D. H. (2002). Brief presurgery hypnosis reduces distress and pain in excisional breast biopsy patients. *International Journal of Clinical and Experimental Hypnosis, 50*(1), 17–32.

Moody, R., & Kubler-Ross, E. (2001). *Life After Life: The Investigation of a Phenomenon—Survival of Bodily Death.* HarperOne.

Moore, L. E., & Kaplan, J. Z. (1983). Hypnotically accelerated burn wound healing. *American Journal of Clinical Hypnosis, 26*(1), 16–19.

Moseley, J. B., O'Malley, K., Petersen, N. J., Menke, T. J., Brody, B. A., Kuykendall, D. H., Wray, N. P., et al. (2002). A controlled trial of arthroscopic surgery for osteoarthritis of the knee. *New England Journal of Medicine, 347*(2), 81–88.

Müller, K., Bacht, K., Schramm, S., & Seitz, R. J. (2012). The facilitating effect of clinical hypnosis on motor imagery: An fMRI study. *Behavioural brain research, 23*(1), 164–169.

Naish, P. L. (2006). Time to explain the nature of hypnosis? *Contemporary Hypnosis, 1*, 33–46.

Nemeth, D., Janacsek, K., Polner, B., & Kovacs, Z. A. (2013). Boosting human learning by hypnosis. *Cerebral Cortex, 23*(4), 801–805.

Newmark, T. (2012). Cases in Visualization for Improved Athletic Performance Psychiatric Annals. *Psychiatric Annals, 42*(10), 385–387.

NIH.gov. (n.d.). Retrieved from http://www.niaid.nih.gov/topics/immunesystem/pages/whatisimmunesystem.aspx

Noble, S. (2002). The management of blood phobia and a hypersensitive gag reflex by hypnotherapy: a case report. *Dental update, 29*(2), 70–74.

Noll, R. B. (1994). Hypnotherapy for warts in children and adolescents. *Journal of Developmental & Behavioral Pediatrics, 15*(3), 170–173.

NYTimes.com. (n.d.). Retrieved from http://www.nytimes.com/2010/08/29/fashion/29PastLives.html?pagewanted=all&_r=0

Page, R. A., & Handley, G. W. (1993). The use of hypnosis in cocaine addiction. *American Journal of Clinical Hypnosis, 36*(2), 120–123.

Page, S. J., Levine, P., Sisto, S., & Johnston, M. V. (2001). A randomized efficacy and feasibility study of imagery in acute stroke. *Clinical Rehabilitation, 15*(3), 233–240.

Partington, P. (2009). Hypnotic interventions for pain management in chiropractic practice: A review. *Clinical Chiropractic, 12*(3), 109–116.

Pates, J. (2013). The Effects of hypnosis on an elite senior european tour golfer: a single-subject design. *International Journal of Clinical and Experimental Hypnosis, 61*(2), 193–204.

Pates, J., Cummings, A., & Maynard, I. (2002). The effects of hypnosis on flow states and three-point shooting performance in basketball players. *Sport Psychologist, 16*(1), 34–47.

Pates, J., Oliver, R., & Maynard, I. (2001). The effects of hypnosis on flow states and golf-putting performance. *Journal of Applied Sport Psychology, 4*, 341–354.

Patterson, D. R., & Jensen, M. P. (2003). Hypnosis and clinical pain. *Psychological Bulletin, 129*(4), 495.

Patterson, D. R., Jensen, M. P., Wiechman, S. A., & Sharar, S. R. (2010). Virtual reality hypnosis for pain associated with recovery from physical trauma. *Intl. Journal of Clinical and Experimental Hypnosis, 58*(3), 288–300.

Perfect, M. M., & Elkins, G. R. (2010). Cognitive–behavioral therapy and hypnotic relaxation to treat sleep problems in an adolescent with diabetes. *Journal of Clinical Psychology, 66*(11), 1205–1215.

Potter, G. (2004). Intensive therapy: utilizing hypnosis in the treatment of substance abuse disorders. *American Journal of Clinical Hypnosis, 47*(1), 21–28.

Quimby, P. P. (2008). *The Quimby Manuscripts.* Forgotten Books.

Quimby, P. P. (2008). *The Quimby Manuscripts.* Forgotten Books.

Radin, D. (1997). *The Conscious Universe.* New York: Harper Collins.

Radin, D. (1997). *The Conscious Universe.* New York: Harper Collins.

Radin, D. (2006). *Entangled Minds.* New york: Pocket Books.

Rainville, P., Hofbauer, R. K., Bushnell, M. C., Duncan, G. H., & Price, D. D. (2002). Hypnosis modulates activity in brain structures involved in the regulation of consciousness. *Journal of Cognitive Neuroscience, 14*(6), 887–901.

Rapkin, D. A., Straubing, M., & Holroyd, J. C. (1991). Guided imagery, hypnosis and recovery from head and neck cancer surgery: an exploratory study. *International journal of clinical and experimental hypnosis, 39*(4), 215–226.

Raz, A., Fan, J., & Posner, M. I. (2005). Hypnotic suggestion reduces conflict in the human brain. *Proceedings of the national Academy of Sciences of the United States of America, 102*(28), 9978–9983.

Rhine, J. B. (1946). Hypnotic suggestion in PK tests. *Journal of Parapsychology.*

Richardson, J., Smith, J. E., McCall, G., Richardson, A., Pilkington, K., & Kirsch, I. (2007). Hypnosis for nausea and vomiting in cancer chemotherapy: a systematic review of the research evidence. *European Journal of Cancer Care, 16*(5), 402–412.

Robazza, C., & Bortoli, L. (1995). A case study of improved performance in archery using hypnosis. *Perceptual and Motor Skills, 81*(3), 1364–1366.

Rock, N. L., Shipley, T. E., & Campbell, C. (1969). Hypnosis with untrained, nonvolunteer patients in labor. *The International Journal of Clinical and Experimental Hypnosis, 17*(1), 25–36.

Rosén, G., Willoch, F., Bartenstein, P., Berner, N., & R∅ sj∅ a, S. (2001). Neurophysiological processes underlying the phantom limb pain experience and the use of hypnosis in its clinical management: An intensive examination of two patients. *International Journal of Clinical and Experimental Hypnosis, 49*(1), 38–55.

Rosen, S. (1997). *The Reincarnation Controversy: Uncovering the truth in the World Religions.* Badger, CA: Torchlight Publishing, Inc.

Rosen, S. (1997). *The Reincarnation COntroversy: Uncovering the truth in the World Religions.* Badger, CA: Torchlight Publishing inc.

Ross, U. H., Lange, O., Unterrainer, J., & Laszig, R. (2007). Ericksonian hypnosis in tinnitus therapy: Effects of a 28-day inpatient multimodal treatment concept measured by Tinnitus-Questionnaire and Health Survey SF-36. *European archives of oto-rhino-laryngology, 264*(5), 483–488.

Salter, A. (1949). *Conditioned reflex therapy, the direct approach to the reconstruction of personality.*

Samuels, N. (2005). Integration of hypnosis with acupuncture: possible benefits and case examples. *American Journal of Clinical Hypnosis, 47*(4), 243–248.

Samuels, N., Sagi, E., Singer, S. R., & Oberbaum, M. (2011). Hypnosis and Acupuncture (Hypnopuncture) for Prurigo Nodularis: A Case Report. *American Journal of Clinical Hypnosis, 53*(4), 277–286.

Sanders, S. (1976). Mutual group hypnosis as a catalyst in fostering creative problem solving. *American Journal of Clinical Hypnosis, 19*(1), 62–66.

Schlebusch, K. P., Maric-Oehler, W., & Popp, F. A. (2005). Biophotonics in the infrared spectral range reveal acupuncture meridian structure of the body. *Journal of Alternative & Complementary Medicine, 11*(1), 171–173.

Schlesinger, I., Benyakov, O., Erikh, I., Suraiya, S., & Schiller, Y. (2009). Parkinson's disease tremor is diminished with relaxation guided imagery. *Movement Disorders, 24*(14), 2059–2062.

Schneck, J. M. (1954). The Hypnotic Trance, Magico-Religious Medicine, and Primitive Initiation Rites. . *Psychoanalytic Review*, 182-190.

Schoen, M., & Nowack, K. (2013). Reconditioning the stress response with hypnosis CD reduces the inflammatory cytokine IL-6 and influences resilience: A pilot study. *Complementary Therapies in Clinical Practice.*

Schoenberger, N. E., Kirsch, I., Gearan, P., Montgomery, G., & Pastyrnak, S. L. (1998). Hypnotic enhancement of a cognitive behavioral treatment for public speaking anxiety. *Behavior Therapy, 28*(1), 127–140.

Schoenberger, N. E., Kirsch, I., Gearan, P., Montgomery, G., & Pastyrnak, S. L. (1998). Hypnotic enhancement of a cognitive behavioral treatment for public speaking anxiety. *Behavior Therapy, 28*(1), 127–140.

SCHREIBER, E. H. (1997). USE OF GROUP HYPNOSIS TO IMPROVE COLLEGE STUDENTS' ACHIEVEMENT. *Psychological reports, 80*(2), 636–638.

Scotton, B., Chinen, A., & Battista, J. (1996). *Textbook Of Transpersonal Psychiatry And Psychology.* New York: Basic Books.

Sheldrake, R. (2012). *Resonance of the Past: Morphic Resonance and The Memory Of Nature.* Rochester: Park Street Press.

Sheldrake, R. (2012). *Science Set Free.* New York: Deepak Chopra Books.

Sheldrake, R. (2012). *Science Set Free: 10 paths To new Discovery.* New York: Deepak Chopra Books.

Sheldrake, R. (2012). *The Presence Of The Past: Morphic Resonance & The Memory Of Nature.* Rochester: Park Street Press.

Sheldrake, R., McKenna, T., & Abraham, R. (2001). *Chaos, Creativity, and Cosmic Consciousness.* Rochester: Park Street Press.

Siegel, B. S. (1998). *Love, medicine & miracles.* New York: William Morrow Paperbacks; Reissue edition.

Siegel, B. S. (1998). *Love, medicine, and miracles.* New York: William Morrow Paperbacks; Reissue edition.

Sokel, B., Christie, D., Kent, A., & Lansdown, R. (1993). A comparison of hypnotherapy and biofeedback in the treatment of childhood atopic eczema. *Contemporary Hypnosis, 10*(3), 145–154.

Spanos, N. (1982). Hypnotic behavior: a cognitive, social, psychological perspective. *Research Communications in Psychology, Psychiatry and Behavior,* 19–213.

Spiegel, D. (2013). Hypnosis and pain control. *In Comprehensive Treatment of Chronic Pain by Medical, Interventional, and Integrative Approaches,* 859–866.

Stanford, R. G., & Stein, A. G. (1994). A meta-analysis of ESP studies contrasting hypnosis and a comparison condition. *Journal of Parapsychology, 58*(3), 235–269.

Steinberg, S. E., Levin, J., & Bell, W. R. (1984). Evidence that less replacement therapy is required for dental extractions in hemophiliacs. *American journal of hematology, 16*(1), 1–13.

Swirsky-Sacchetti, T., & Margolis, C. G. (1986). The effects of a comprehensive self-hypnosis training program on the use of Factor VIII in severe hemophilia. *The International journal of clinical and experimental hypnosis, 34*(2), 71–83.

Syrjala, K. L., Cummings, C., & Donaldson, G. W. (1992). Hypnosis or cognitive behavioral training for the reduction of pain and nausea during cancer treatment: a controlled clinical trial. Pain. *Pain, 48*(2), 137–146.

Talbot, M. (1991). *The Holographic universe.* New York: Harper Collins.

Talbot, M. (1991). *The Holographic universe.* New York: Harper Collins.

Talbot, M. (1991). *The Holographic Universe.* New York: Harper Collins.

Tan, G., Fukui, T., Jensen, M. P., Thornby, J., & Waldman, K. L. (2009). Hypnosis treatment for chronic low back pain. *Intl. Journal of Clinical and Experimental Hypnosis, 58*(1), 53–68.

Tart, C. T. (1967). Psychedelic experiences associated with a novel hypnotic procedure, mutual hypnosis. *American Journal of Clinical Hypnosis, 10*(2), 65–78.

Tart, C. T. (1970). Transpersonal potentialities of deep hypnosis. *Transpersonal Psych, 2*(1).

Tart, C. T. (1998). Six studies of out-of-body experiences. *Journal of Near-Death Studies, 17*(2), 73-99.

Tausk, F., & Whitmore, S. E. (1999). A pilot study of hypnosis in the treatment of patients with psoriasis. *Psychotherapy and Psychosomatics, 68*(4), 221–225.

Teeley, A. M., Soltani, M., Wiechman, S. A., Jensen, M. P., Sharar, S. R., & Patterson, D. R. (2012). Virtual reality hypnosis pain control in the treatment of multiple fractures: a case series 1. *American Journal of Clinical Hypnosis, 54*(3), 184–194.

Tressoldi, P., & Del Prete, G. (2007). ESP under hypnosis: The role of induction instructions and personality characteristics. *Journal of Parapsychology*, 71,125.

uoregon.edu. (n.d.). Retrieved from http://abyss.uoregon.edu/~js/21st_century_science/lectures/lec14.html

van Quekelberghe, R., GÃķbel, P., & Hertweck, E. (1995). Simulation of near-death and out-of-body experiences under hypnosis. *Imagination, Cognition and Personality*.

Vandenbergh, R. L., Sussman, K. E., & Titus, C. C. (1966). Effects of hypnotically induced acute emotional stress on carbohydrate and lipid metabolism in patients with diabetes mellitus. *Psychosomatic Medicine, 4*, 382–390.

Velloso, L. G., Duprat, M. D., Martins, R., & Scoppetta, L. (2010). Hypnosis for management of claustrophobia in magnetic resonance imaging. *Radiologia Brasileira, 43*(1), 19–22.

Volpe, E. G., & Nash, M. R. (2012). The use of hypnosis for airplane phobia with an obsessive character a case study. *Clinical Case Studies, 11*(2), 89–103.

Wain, H. J., Amen, D., & Jabbari, B. (1990). The effects of hypnosis on a parkinsonian tremor: case report with polygraph/EEG recordings. *American Journal of Clinical Hypnosis, 33*(2), 94–98.

Ward, N. S., Oakley, D. A., Frackowiak, R. S., & Halligan, P. W. (2003). Differential brain activations during intentionally simulated and subjectively experienced paralysis. *Cognitive Neuropsychiatry, 8*(4), 295–312.

Warner, D. A., Barabasz, A. F., & Barabasz, M. (2000). The efficacy of barabasz's alert hypnosis and neurotherapy on attentiveness, impulsivity and hyperactivity in children with ADHD. *Child Study Journal, 30*(1), 43–49.

Warner, D. A., Barabasz, A. F., & Barabasz, M. (2000). The Efficacy of Barabasz's Alert Hypnosis and Neurotherapy on Attentiveness, Impulsivity and Hyperactivity in Children with ADHD. Child Study Journal. *Child Study Journal, 30*(1), 43–49.

Weil, A. (2000). *Spontaneous Healing*. New York: The Random House Publishing Group.

Weil, A., & Gurgevich, S. (2005, September 1). Heal Yourself with Medical Hypnosis: The Most Immediate Way to Use Your Mind-Body Connection. Sounds True, Incorporated; Unabridged edition.

Weinstein, E. J., & Au, P. K. (1991). Use of hypnosis before and during angioplasty. *American Journal of Clinical Hypnosis, 34*(1), 29–37.

Weiss, B. L. (1988). *Many Lives, Many Masters*. New York: Fireside.

Whitton, J., & Fisher, J. (1987). *Life Between Life*. London: Grafton; New Ed edition.

Whitton, J., & Fisher, J. (1987). *Life Between Life*. London: Grafton; New Ed edition.

Wik, G. F. (1999). Functional anatomy of hypnotic analgesia: a PET study of patients with fibromyalgia. European Journal of Pain. *European Journal of Pain, 3*(1), 7–12.

Willard, R. D. (1977). Breast enlargement through visual imagery and hypnosis. *American Journal of Clinical Hypnosis, 19*(4), 195-200.

Willemsen, R., Vanderlinden, J., Deconinck, A., & Roseeuw, D. (2006). Hypnotherapeutic management of alopecia areata. *Journal of the American Academy of Dermatology, 55*(2), 233-237.

Williams, J. D., & Gruzelier, J. H. (2001). Differentiation of hypnosis and relaxation by analysis of narrow band theta and alpha frequencies. *International Journal of Clinical and Experimental Hypnosis, 49*(3), 185–206.

Williams, J. E. (1974). Stimulation of breast growth by hypnosis. *Journal of Sex Research, 10*(4), 316–326.

Wood, G. J., Bughi, S., Morrison, J., Tanavoli, S., Tanavoli, S., & Zadeh, H. H. (2003). Hypnosis, differential expression of cytokines by T-cell subsets, and the hypothalamo-pituitary-adrenal axis. *American Journal of Clinical Hypnosis, 45*(3), 179–196.

Wu, M. T., Sheen, J. M., Chuang, K. H., Yang, P., Chin, S. L., Tsai, C. Y., & Yang, C. F. (2002). Neuronal specificity of acupuncture response: a fMRI study with electroacupuncture. *Neuroimage, 16*(4), 1028–1037.

Xu, Y., & Cardeña, E. (2007). Hypnosis as an adjunct therapy in the management of diabetes. *Intl. Journal of Clinical and Experimental Hypnosis, 56*(1), 63–72.

Yapko, M. D. (1993). Hypnosis and depression. *Handbook of Clinical Hypnosis*, 339–355.

Yapko, M. D. (2010). Hypnosis in the treatment of depression: An overdue approach for encouraging skillful mood management. *Intl. Journal of Clinical and Experimental Hypnosis, 58*(2), 137–146.

Yapko, M. D. (2010). Hypnotically catalyzing experiential learning across treatments for depression: Actions can speak louder than moods. *Intl. Journal of Clinical and Experimental Hypnosis, 58*(2), 186–201.

Yexley, M. J. (2007). Treating postpartum depression with hypnosis: Addressing specific symptoms presented by the client. *American Journal of Clinical Hypnosis, 49*(3), 219–223.

Zachariae, R., Bjerring, P., & Arendt-Nielsen, L. (1989). Modulation of type I immediate and type IV delayed immunoreactivity using direct suggestion and guided imagery during hypnosis. *Allergy, 44*(8), 537–542.

Zeltzer, L., Dash, J., & Holland, J. P. (1979). Hypnotically induced pain control in sickle cell anemia. *Pediatrics, 64*(4), 533–536.

CPSIA information can be obtained at www.ICGtesting.com
Printed in the USA
BVOW02*1823070415

395120BV00005BA/7/P

9 780692 315989